THE RISE OF THE AMERICAN CHEMISTRY PROFESSION, 1850-1900

by Edward H. Beardsley

University of Florida Monographs

SOCIAL SCIENCES

No. 23, Summer 1964

UNIVERSITY OF FLORIDA PRESS / GAINESVILLE, FLORIDA

INTRODUCTION

In 1850 Americans had enjoyed over fifty years of political independence, but in other spheres the United States remained Europe's colony. The national economy was still extractive, depending largely on European purchases of raw cotton to provide foreign credits. As a developing nation the United States had deficiencies of heavy manufactured goods and investment capital, both of which the Old World had to supply. In the arts, particularly in music, architecture, and painting, Europe set American standards. While this nation could boast individuals who had shown great originality, in most matters of culture and taste America continued to be an imitative country.

In science the United States relied almost completely on Europe. This dependence was particularly apparent in the field of chemistry. Students and professionals looked to Europe for both the tools and the ideas of the discipline. American chemists remained a step or two behind those in Europe, relying on students returning from abroad and on foreign reports in the few American scientific journals for word of new theoretical developments.

If 1850 saw American chemists playing a dependent role, changes were in prospect. In the next half-century chemists succeeded in erecting the professional institutions they needed to make them self-sufficient. Aided by demands from industry for wider dissemination of applied knowledge, American scientists created an undergraduate educational system capable of imparting known principles and techniques to students in chemistry. With the German example to guide them, workers also built a network of graduate departments in which young men could train themselves for research careers. In the same half-century chemists also labored to create specialized journals and professional societies which proved effective in promoting research, giving efficiency and unity to the national effort, and setting values for the profession.

American chemists needed a secure position in the economy just as much as they needed professional institutions. By the first decade of the twentieth century reforms in higher education, an expanding government bureaucracy, and the rise of national industries all combined to give chemists an assured place in the occupational structure of American society.

This monograph is an institutional history of chemistry in the United States. It rests on the premise that science derives many of its goals, its institutional forms, and its support from the larger society of which it is a part. I have not attempted to write a history of the development of chemical knowledge. The existence and expansion of a body of knowledge is basic to any profession, but I feel justified in excluding internal, technical history for two reasons. First, this is a history of American activity, and in the period under study the major theoretical advances were made by Europeans. Second, sound histories of the growth of chemical knowledge already exist, including a few accounts of American theoretical work.

I wish to express my appreciation to three men who offered help and guidance in the preparation of this study. Assistant Professor Charles Rosenberg, Department of History, University of Pennsylvania, gave me the benefit of his wide knowledge of the institutional development of American science and supplied good counsel at crucial times. Professor Aaron Ihde, who teaches the history of science at the University of Wisconsin, read my manuscript along the way and made numerous helpful criticisms. I owe the greatest debt to Professor Irvin G. Wyllie of the Wisconsin Department of History for the stimulation and encouragement he gave to the writing of this essay. My thanks are due to him particularly for his patience as I struggled with the task of forging the tools of the historian from those of the engineer. Finally, my thanks are extended to the Graduate School of the University of Florida for making this publication possible.

Houghton Mifflin Company kindly gave permission to quote from the *Autobiography of Andrew Carnegie,* and Yale University Press generously allowed quotation from Elizabeth Osborne, *From the Files of Samuel W. Johnson.*

EDWARD H. BEARDSLEY

University of Wisconsin

CONTENTS

1. EDUCATION IN CHEMISTRY: AMERICAN ORIGINS

In the middle decades of the nineteenth century, popular dissatisfaction with a higher educational system wed to the culture of ancient Greece and Rome was at its height. Americans not planning careers in medicine, law, or the ministry shared a feeling that the classical college had little to offer. The collegiate curriculum of that day was almost totally devoted to Greek, Latin, mathematics, and moral philosophy. Subjects having practical application, such as engineering, chemistry, agricultural science, physics, and geology, if taught at all, received only slight attention. Even where scientific instruction was offered, teaching laboratories were practically unknown. As a result many Americans who were engaged in the work of building railroads, exploiting natural resources, increasing agricultural production, and setting up an industrial establishment began to insist that the United States had pressing educational needs of a noncultural kind.

As early as the 1840's colleges began to feel the effects of their remoteness from and indifference to the material interests of the American people. In 1850 President Francis Wayland of Brown University reported to his trustees that college enrollment was not only failing to keep pace with the expanding American population, but was actually experiencing a decline. From 1840 to 1850 total attendance at twelve New England colleges and universities had dropped from 2,063 to 1,884. Wayland said that the reason for the decline was plain: Colleges "are not filled, because we do not furnish the education desired by the people. . . . Even when we give it away, still the demand diminishes."[1] Not all colleges could give their services away; those that could not suffered a harsh fate. In the years before 1860, declining student enrollment was a factor in forcing over 700 colleges to close their doors.[2] Colleges began to see that the only hope of re-establishing their connection with the

1. Report to the Brown Corporation, 1850, quoted in Francis Amasa Walker, *Discussions in Education* (New York, 1899), 82. See S. D. Ross, *Democracy's Colleges* (Ames, Iowa, 1942), 15; Richard Hofstadter and D. C. Hardy, *The Development and Scope of Higher Education in the United States* (New York, 1952), 29.
2. Frederick Rudolph, *The American College and University* (New York, 1962), 219.

American people and of restoring their financial position lay in making greater provision for studies promising immediate utility. The rise of chemistry as an academic subject reflected the colleges' growing willingness to pay heed to popular demands.

The Sheffield Scientific School of Yale College (initially called the Department of Philosophy and the Arts), the Lawrence Scientific School of Harvard College, and Harvard College itself led the way in giving chemistry a respected place in American higher education. These early chemistry departments set the pattern and prepared the ground for later developments in American chemical education. Their success was largely due to the individual efforts of a handful of pioneer American chemists.[3]

In 1846 Benjamin Silliman, Sr., Yale professor of chemistry, and his son and assistant, Benjamin Silliman, Jr., petitioned the Yale Corporation to found a school of applied chemistry. Arguing that the college should recognize the educational needs of the large number of Americans planning to make their living in agriculture and manufacturing, the Sillimans asked the Yale trustees to provide a laboratory and establish professorships of agricultural and applied chemistry. The petitioners testified that because of a lack of facilities they had turned away many students who had come to them seeking advanced instruction in chemistry. These students either had to give up their professional ambitions or go to European universities, since no American university offered advanced training in chemistry at that time.[4]

After a period of deliberation the Yale Corporation in 1847 established the Department of Philosophy and the Arts to embrace all branches not included under theology, medicine, or law. Faithful to the Sillimans' request, the corporation included the School

3. Early efforts to establish systems of chemical education at Harvard and Yale did not represent the first provision for instruction in chemistry. American colleges had established chairs of chemistry in the late eighteenth century. What made these mid-nineteenth-century chemical departments unique was that they were the first to offer a student of chemistry a full program of chemical studies, including laboratory practice. There were other centers of chemical education which evolved about the same time as the departments in New Haven and Cambridge, such as the Chandler Scientific School of Dartmouth College and the University of Michigan's Department of Literature, Science, and the Arts. These departments did not have as much influence as the chemistry programs at Harvard and Yale, nor did they attract students or staff of the same calibre.

4. John F. Fulton and Elizabeth Thomson, *Benjamin Silliman, 1779-1864: Pathfinder in American Science* (New York, 1947), 206-9.

of Applied Chemistry in the new department and created the professorships that the Sillimans had specified. Benjamin Silliman, Jr., received the post of Professor of Chemistry as Applied to the Arts, and John Pitkin Norton, formerly a special student of chemistry under the Sillimans, Professor of Agricultural Chemistry.[5]

The Silliman and Norton appointments carried no salary. The college cautioned the new professors that it did not expect to bear any of the financial burdens of the chemistry school. It did provide a laboratory for chemical instruction (a house that had served as the president's residence), but on a rent basis and only after Norton and Silliman assured Yale President Woolsey that no "danger from fire need be feared," and that "no change or injury" to the house would result from its use as a laboratory.[6]

Students in the new department had no official connection with Yale College. The corporation legislated to prevent contact between regular college students and those in the philosophy department. For the most part courses in the college were not open to philosophy department students, and vice versa. Students of the new department could not live in the college dormitory nor were they welcome at the chapel services. Furthermore, there would be no degrees for students in the new department: it must first prove itself worthy of the Yale diploma.[7]

By 1847 Norton and Silliman had developed a program of studies. Norton lectured on agricultural chemistry and Silliman gave a course in industrial chemistry. In the analytical laboratory students got the chance to practice what they had learned.[8]

Meeting expenses proved a difficult task. John T. Norton, the young professor's father, anonymously gave $5,000 to support the new enterprise.[9] But that gift provided only a fraction of the endowment needed, and professors Norton and Silliman had to rely on their own resources to meet initial costs.[10] In the first year

5. *Catalogue of the Officers and Students in Yale College*, 1846-47:42, 1847-48:4.

6. John Norton and Benjamin Silliman, Jr., c. 1847, to President Woolsey, Yale Memorabilia Collection, Yale University.

7. Yale Catalogue, 1847-48:42-43.   8. *Ibid.*

9. Howard S. Miller, "A Bounty for Research. The Philanthropic Support of Scientific Investigation in America, 1838-1902" (Typescript Ph.D. thesis, University of Wisconsin, 1964), 157.

10. Norton and Silliman, April 10, 1848, to Yale Corporation; c. 1849, to Yale President and Corporation; c. 1850, to Yale Prudential Committee, Yale Memorabilia Collection.

they expended $2,000 of their own funds for equipment and chemicals. Operating expenses, far outrunning student fees, posed another problem. Ever resourceful, the two chemists found a solution in outside consulting work. They analyzed dried fish for a man interested in its commercial fertilizer value and a piece of India rubber for a young inventor named Charles Goodyear.[11]

By 1849 financial matters were fairly well in hand, the number of students was rising, and the two professors viewed their success as "far beyond our expectations."[12] That year, however, saw the first serious challenge to the infant scientific school: Silliman departed for a teaching post at the University of Louisville.[13] Had John Norton been a man of small talent and dedication, Silliman's leaving might have been crucial. Norton, however, was determined to make the institution a "credit . . . to the country," and though forced to work under a heavy strain, he seemed completely tireless.[14] Besides giving nearly all the instruction, he worked energetically to "sell" the school and to find jobs for its students. Yet he always managed time for students' problems: his concern that they have suitable living accommodations was characteristic of his interest in their welfare.[15]

In 1850 Norton urged the Yale Corporation to reconsider its position on degrees for his department. Awarding the bachelor's and doctor's degrees would induce students to prolong their stay in the laboratory and enhance its reputation. The college could grant the higher awards without fear of sullying its standing, Norton argued, for students of the School of Applied Chemistry had won creditable positions for themselves.[16] In 1851, after a year of pressing his case, Norton achieved a partial victory: Yale agreed to

11. Norton, April 14, 1848, to Charles D. Miller; March 29, 1849, to F. G. Parke; December 15, 1848, to Philip Galpin; April 19, 1849 to Charles Goodyear; Yale Analytical Laboratory Letter Press Book, Yale University Library, microfilm in Wisconsin Historical Society Library, Madison.

12. Norton, October 7, 1848, to S. T. Rogers, Yale Analyt. Lab. Letter Press Book; see Yale Catalogue, 1847-48, 1849-50.

13. Silliman continued to instruct at the applied chemistry school in the summers, but for all practical purposes he was out of the picture by the fall of 1849.

14. June 7, 1849, to Oliver Wolcott Gibbs, Yale Analyt. Lab. Letter Press Book.

15. Norton, November 16, 1848, to Peter Curtiss; April 8, 1851, to Charles B. Stuart; January 23, 1851, to J. Burnell, Yale Analyt. Lab. Letter Press Book.

16. December 10, 1850, to Yale Prudential Committee; c. 1851, to Yale President, Corporation, and Fellows, Yale Memorabilia Collection.

grant the Bachelor of Philosophy degree to students of the new department.[17]

In the fall of 1852 death ended John Norton's career. Only thirty years old when he died, he succumbed to pneumonia contracted during the winter of 1851-52 when he had taken on the extra burden of traveling to Albany, New York, every week to aid in the establishment of a university there. According to his father, Norton "remembered his laboratory . . . in his dying moments, expressing the earnest wish that it might be continued, and requesting that if it were continued all his property therein . . . should be given to Yale College."[18]

The laboratory and the school continued. From 1852 to 1855 the instructional staff and curriculum of the School of Applied Chemistry expanded measurably. In 1853 John A. Porter, a graduate of Giessen University, took Norton's place as professor of agricultural chemistry. Two years later George J. Brush and Samuel W. Johnson joined the faculty. Brush returned from a period of study at Munich and Freiberg universities to take up a post in mineralogy, and Johnson, also trained at Munich, became first assistant in the chemistry laboratory.[19] These young men entered their work with great enthusiasm. Brush told Johnson while still in Germany that he thought they would "be able to do 'some pumpkins,' if not more," when "we all get back and start our team in good earnest."[20]

In 1854 Yale College acknowledged that the new program of scientific studies had achieved respectability by renaming the Department of Philosophy the Yale Scientific School.[21] Her name however, was all that Yale would give. The chemistry program continued to lack an endowment, and the expansion in courses and faculty, by attracting more students, put an added strain on

17. Yale Catalogue, 1851-52:45.
18. John T. Norton, January 12, 1853, to President Woolsey, Yale Memorabilia Collection. Also see "Obituary," *American Journal of Science and Arts,* 14 (1853), 448-49.
19. Yale Catalogue, 1852-53:4; 1855-56:13; "Obituary of John A. Porter," *American Journal of Science and Arts* (1867), 290; "George J. Brush," *National Cyclopaedia of American Biography,* 10:298; T. B. Osborne, "S. W. Johnson," National Academy of Sciences, *Biographical Memoirs,* 7 (1913), 193-222.
20. Elizabeth A. Osborne, *From the Letter Files of Samuel W. Johnson* (New Haven, 1918), 93.
21. Russell H. Chittenden, *History of the Sheffield Scientific School* (2 volumes, New Haven, 1928), 1:71-72; Yale Catalogue, 1854-55:50; 1855-56:53.

existing facilities and income. By the mid-1850's some of the faculty began to lose their enthusiasm and look for other positions. In 1856, viewing the run-down condition of the laboratory and the lack of books, Samuel Johnson concluded that the Yale Scientific School was on the verge of failure.[22]

Aware of the pressing needs of the new institution, the scientific community of Yale College launched an all-out effort to obtain an adequate endowment. Although appeals were made at commencements and in the periodical press, the campaign—with but one exception—was a failure: Joseph Sheffield, New Haven industrialist, gave $5000 to purchase a new building for the chemistry laboratory. While that gift allowed the establishment of a more complete experimental course, including original investigations, it did not solve the problem of insufficient operating revenue.[23]

In 1859 hope for endowment appeared from a new quarter. Senator Justin Morrill introduced before Congress an agricultural bill which promised support for institutions giving instruction in agricultural science. Hope faded, however, as it became apparent that President Buchanan would reject the measure. Benjamin Silliman, Jr., now back in New Haven, expressed the frustration of Yale chemists when he asked a Pennsylvania friend, "Cannot your old statesman who now holds the trembling goose quil [sic] ready to veto Morrill's Agriculture Bill be made to feel the force of opinion from the rural districts . . . as against this last act of imbecile folly?"[24] Buchanan vetoed the bill as predicted, and 1860 promised to be a crucial year for chemical education at the Yale Scientific School. Hope for federal assistance was gone, the college would offer no help, and there was no prospect of state aid. The chemistry faculty was frankly worried about the school's survival.[25]

What promised to be a bleak year proved to be a good one. Joseph Sheffield's long interest in practical science education and the Yale Scientific School (partly because his son-in-law, John Porter, was professor of agricultural chemistry there) led him to see

22. Chittenden, 1:71-72; E. A. Osborne, 92-93, 125-26, 103.
23. Chittenden, 1:65-70, 71-72; E. A. Osborne, 132-33; Yale Catalogue 1856-57:45. See D. C. Gilman, "Scientific Schools in Europe," *American Journal of Education*, 1 (1855), 315-28; John A. Porter, "Plan of an Agricultural School," *American Journal of Education*, 1 (1855), 329-35.
24. March 7, 1859, to W. H. Brewer, Yale Memorabilia Collection.
25. E. A. Osborne, 132-33.

6

finally that the school could not hope to prosper without large means. In 1860 he agreed to give an endowment of $100,000. This money provided a new laboratory and gave the chemical department an ample income for the first time. Financial stability led to a complete overhaul of the course and degree program. In 1860 the Yale Scientific School offered the chemistry student a three-year undergraduate course, plus a Ph.D. for advanced work.[26]

In 1863 additional support came to the Sheffield Scientific School (renamed for its benefactor in 1862) when Connecticut made it the beneficiary of the 1862 Morrill Act grant. Providing funds for basic as well as applied sciences, the grant provided additional operating revenue, new professorships, and student scholarships. Chemistry and engineering, the most popular programs in the school, got the bulk of the new support.[27]

The Lawrence Scientific School at Harvard College, unlike its counterpart at Yale, was fortunate enough to have sufficient endowment at the outset. In June, 1847, Abbott Lawrence, a New England railroad builder, cotton manufacturer, and merchant, gave $50,000 to endow scientific and technical education at Harvard. Lawrence's experience had convinced him that skilled engineers and chemists were vital to the success of American industry. His work in cotton manufacturing had shown him that the development of adequate water power required the service of a trained engineer, and that bleacheries and printworks sorely needed skilled chemists.[28]

Harvard College used the Lawrence gift to endow a separate school of science, applying one-half of the money for a chemistry laboratory. German-trained scientist Eben N. Horsford became the first chemistry professor in the Lawrence Scientific School. As his interests tended strongly toward applied chemistry, his course program reflected those leanings.[29] Opening his laboratory in 1848, Horsford gave instruction in chemical analysis as applied to manu-

26. Chittenden, 1:71-72; Yale Catalogue, 1860-61:45-54.

27. Chittenden, 1:236. See Silliman, January 24, 1863, to W. H. Brewer, Yale Memorabilia Collection; Chittenden, 1:91-92, 101, 118.

28. Charles W. Eliot, *Harvard Memories* (Cambridge, 1923), 57-58; R. J. Storr, *The Beginnings of Graduate Education in America* (Chicago, 1953), 49: Chittenden, 1:38; Samuel Eliot Morison, *Three Centuries of Harvard, 1636-1936* (Cambridge, 1937), 279-80.

29. *National Cyclopaedia of American Biography,* 7:55-56; Charles Loring Jackson, "Eben Horsford," American Academy of Arts and Sciences, *Proceedings,* 28 (1893), 342-43.

facturing, metallurgy, medicine, and agriculture. After mastering basic analytical methods, students learned to run tests for poisons, analyze water, and manufacture drugs and manures. Visits to local chemical establishments were a part of the schedule, while lectures in applied and theoretical chemistry completed Horsford's program.

In 1851 and 1852 Horsford enlarged his laboratory course. The offering of instruction in the "solution of problems of research in experimental science" indicated that Horsford's course was not to be geared totally to applied chemistry.[30] In 1852 Harvard granted the Bachelor of Science degree to students completing a year's study and passing an examination in their major field.[31]

In the mid-1850's Charles F. Chandler, later to pioneer in chemical education at the Columbia College School of Mines, became a Lawrence School student. His experience suggested that Horsford's program looked much better in the catalogue than it actually was. Eager to study with Horsford, Chandler found that the chemist gave only part time to his academic work, devoting much of his attention to a chemical firm he had founded in 1853. Lack of guidance was also a disappointment. After a hurried introduction to qualitative and quantitative analysis, students were simply "turned loose in the laboratory" to look after themselves.[32] As Horsford was no longer even giving his lectures, students had to make independent home study serve in place of formal instruction. Another of Chandler's complaints was that the scientific school students were virtually forbidden to enter the college gates. In general Harvard followed the same policy of academic segregation as Yale.[33]

In 1863 Eben Horsford left the Lawrence Scientific School to devote full time to his manufacturing firm. German-trained Ph.D. Oliver Wolcott Gibbs replaced him. Though he made few changes in the curriculum, Gibbs put such stress on basic research that the chemical work of the scientific school took on a whole, new tone. An active researcher in his own right, Gibbs stimulated a like enthusiasm among his students, often parcelling out portions of

30. *Catalogue of the Officers and Students of Harvard University,* 1851-52:72. see *ibid.,* 1848-49:59-60, 1852-53:74; M. V. Bail, *View of Harvard* (Cambridge, 1949), 229-30.
31. Harvard Catalogue, 1851-52:71.
32. M. T. Bogert, "C. F. Chandler," National Academy, *Biographical Memoirs,* 14 (1932), 130-31.   33. *Ibid.*

his own experiments to promising pupils. While assistants attended to routine instruction, Gibbs guided advanced scholars, checking their investigations and challenging them to think for themselves. Chemist Frank W. Clarke, reflecting on the fruitful years he spent with Gibbs, asserted that his former mentor, more than any other man, introduced the German concept of research into America.[34]

In 1850 Josiah Parsons Cooke accepted the post of instructor in chemistry at Harvard College, full of plans to build a flourishing program of chemical studies there. This promised to be no easy task because in 1850 chemistry was defunct at Harvard. There was no laboratory for teacher or pupil, nor did the college own a single piece of chemical apparatus. Even lectures in chemistry had disappeared from the curriculum, because there was no one to give them. In a celebrated murder trial in 1849 Harvard's professor of chemistry, John Webster, was found guilty of the brutal slaying of a Boston physician and was hanged for his crime.[35]

If Josiah Cooke found little tradition in chemistry to build upon, he was not without supporters for his work. He could count on the assistance of popular opinion to back his efforts to loosen up the rigid Harvard curriculum. About the time that Cooke assumed his position at Harvard, George S. Boutwell, a Massachusetts Democratic leader, attacked Harvard for its indifference to the practical concerns of life. Reporting to a state legislative committee which was investigating the college, Boutwell charged that the Harvard curriculum was twenty-five years behind the times. He accused the institution of failing to "answer the just expectations of the people of the state." Harvard College should have been trying to make better "farmers, mechanics, and merchants," Boutwell said, but instead it was offering instruction better suited to an aristocracy.[36]

Cooke, like Boutwell, wanted Harvard College to meet the needs of the people of the state, but his youth (he was twenty-three when he took up his Harvard post), low academic rank, and inexperience seemed to limit his fitness to do battle with the classical tradition in education. However, he had two things in his favor. He was a

34. F. W. Clarke, "Oliver Wolcott Gibbs,'" National Academy, *Memoirs*, 7 (1913), 10; see *ibid.*, pp. 1-22; Harvard Catalogue, 1863-72.
35. Harvard Catalogue, 1849-50, 1850-51:5; Morison, 282-86; C. L. Jackson, *et al.*, "Josiah Parsons Cooke," American Academy *Proceedings*, 30 (1895), 514-15.
36. Quoted in Morison, 287.

close friend of Harvard President Jared Sparks. This personal tie meant that his proposals regarding education in chemistry would receive a sympathetic hearing from at least one member of the Harvard Corporation. Cooke's other asset was his persistence. He sent letter after letter to corporation meetings until that body found it "difficult to resist the frequent demands of the young Professor."[37]

Cooke's polite agitation paid off. Before the end of his first year he gained approval to add two courses to the one he contracted to teach. His energy also won him an appointment to the vacant chemistry chair, boosting his standing and providing him with added income which he could use to advance his work. In succeeding years he continued to strive toward an expanded curriculum, until by 1856 he was offering five courses in chemistry—a sharp contrast to the complete absence of courses in 1850.[38]

Aware that mere courses had little value without accompanying experimental practice, Cooke began to campaign for a teaching laboratory as soon as he came to Harvard. Knowing that college trustees did not share his views, his initial demands were modest. All he wanted was a small private laboratory in which he could train a few students. In 1850 the college gave him a basement storeroom and told him that he would have to provide chemicals at his own expense.[39] Luckily for the progress of chemistry at Harvard, Cooke had sufficient private resources to outfit his early laboratory.[40]

That first laboratory served him well as a place to prepare demonstration experiments, but Cooke wanted to bring the student to the apparatus rather than the apparatus to the student. This would not only make the learning process more efficient, but it would save Cooke a great deal of wasted effort. His responsibility for lectures in the medical school in Boston as well as those in the college at Cambridge, turned Cooke into a kind of academic teamster: several times a week he had to make the tedious trip between the two points with a cartload of bulky and fragile apparatus.[41]

In 1856 Cooke decided to force the issue of a teaching laboratory.

37. Jackson, 533.
38. *Ibid.*, 534; Harvard Catalogue, 1850-51:41-44, 48; 1853-54:26, 29, 30-31.
39. Jackson, 514-15.
40. *Ibid.*, 530-31, 534.
41. *Ibid.*, 516.

His plan involved the use of the Boylston fund which had been accumulating at Harvard since 1818. Ward Nicholas Boylston left an endowment for an anatomical museum and chemistry laboratory but, by the terms of the gift, construction had to be deferred until the fund reached $35,000. Although in 1856 the total of the endowment was only $23,000, Cooke proposed that if the college would release the fund for its stated purpose, he would raise the balance. In January, 1857, after deliberating for several months, the corporation agreed to Cooke's plan, with the proviso that the professor raise not $12,000 but $17,000. Cooke had been soliciting money while the corporation was deliberating, and in less than a month after gaining approval for his scheme he was able to report that he had raised the full amount. Astounded and pleased by the young professor's drive, the college released the Boylston funds.[42]

In 1858 the laboratory was opened for instruction. Its completion permitted Cooke to make new inroads on the curriculum. That year he offered the first student laboratory course at Harvard College. By 1859 he had succeeded in giving the college a strong chemistry program. He had injected seven chemistry courses into a tradition-bound curriculum, and, thanks largely to his efforts, Harvard was one of the first of the "old" institutions to have a teaching laboratory.[43]

The pioneer chemistry departments at the Sheffield and Lawrence Scientific schools and within Harvard College had a great influence on the development of facilities and programs elsewhere. The 1850's and 1860's saw the establishment of a host of schools patterned after the Lawrence and Sheffield examples. Among them were the Chandler Scientific School of Dartmouth College, the Brooklyn Polytechnic School, the Massachusetts Institute of Technology, the Columbia College School of Mines, and the Pardee Scientific School of Lafayette College.[44] The work of Josiah Cooke was also influential. Cooke helped to win for the sciences a place in the college curriculum equal to that held by the classics. He also helped to secure for students of the sciences the same rank and privileges as other college students. Although the Lawrence and

42. Ibid., 539; see ibid., 536, 538-39; Bail, 241-42.
43. John Hays Gardiner, Harvard (New York, 1914), 46-47; Harvard Catalogue, 1859-60:30-31.
44. Rudolph, 232-33. In the decade of the 1860's over twenty scientific schools were founded. See Report of the Commissioner of Education, 1885-1886 (Washington, 1887), 532-33.

Sheffield Scientific School pattern of a segregated existence exerted more influence on the shape of education in chemistry in the beginning, the Harvard College example of equal treatment commanded more attention after the initial momentum of the scientific school movement had spent itself. When Cornell University opened its doors in 1868, chemistry and other sciences had a place in its curriculum equal to that of nonscientific subjects.[45]

These first programs in chemistry furnished the personnel to staff the later chemistry departments. Josiah Cooke's students, Charles W. Eliot and Frank Storer, were the first directors of the analytical laboratory at the Massachusetts Institute of Technology. Sheffield student William Blake taught mining chemistry at the University of California, and later graduate Peter Collier held a chemistry professorship at the University of Vermont. Chemistry students of the Lawrence Scientific School taught at the University of Wisconsin, Cornell University, and M.I.T., to cite but a few examples.[46]

The factors contributing to the success of the earliest chemical programs continued to operate beyond the formative years. Popular demands for a higher education attuned to the practical pursuits, Morrill Act grants, and the philanthropy of merchants and industrialists remained key elements in expanding the facilities for education in chemistry in America.

By the 1870's the American student could find some 60 colleges, universities, and scientific schools which offered at least three years of instruction in chemistry.[47] In effect, America had created a national system of chemical education. It was a system largely concerned with the dissemination and application of knowledge, and in that respect not comparable with the systems of chemical education in Germany, or even France. Nevertheless,

45. Andrew D. White, *Autobiography* (2 volumes, New York, 1905), 1:341. The work that Cooke did for chemistry, other scholars did for other "forbidden" studies, such as modern languages, American history, economics, English literature. The electoral system (especially after C. W. Eliot gave it such standing at Harvard) furthered the work of such academic pioneers as Josiah Cooke, by giving them greater freedom to set up courses, and by offering the student freedom to select them.

46. Jackson, 541; *National Cyclopedia*, 10:40, 8:356; G. F. Bush, "History of Higher Education in Massachusetts," *Circular of Information Number 6, U. S. Bureau of Education* (Washington, 1891), 117.

47. F. W. Clarke, *A Report of the Teaching of Chemistry and Physics and Chemistry in the United States, Circular of the Bureau of Education, 1880* (Washington, 1881), 167-68, Table II.

by the 1870's American chemistry departments were capable of providing a supply of trained chemists to fill the increasing number of positions in educational institutions, government agencies, and industry. If American education in chemistry was not yet research-minded, as the German system was, it was able to prepare the American student to profit by German training.

2. EDUCATION IN CHEMISTRY:
THE GERMAN INFLUENCE

In the years between 1850 and World War I nearly 10,000 American students matriculated in German universities; about one-tenth of them were seeking advanced instruction in chemistry.[1] The most popular German institution for such students was the University of Berlin, but the universities of Göttingen and Heidelberg and the Freiberg Mining Academy followed closely.[2]

The German university attracted young American chemistry students for several reasons.[3] Many students went to Germany because it was fashionable to do so, and because German training was an index of culture. As one observer put it, "upper class students in the United States don't think their education finished until they have their *Wanderjahr* (or two) in a German university."[4] Through most of the nineteenth century the universities of Germany offered

1. For estimates of the number of American students in German universities, see Charles F. Thwing, *The American and the German University* (New York, 1928), 140-41. In estimating chemists, I have used figures for chemistry students at Göttingen University in D. B. Shumway, "American Students at the University of Göttingen," *German-American Annals*, 8 (January, February, 1910), 199-251, and H. S. Van Klooster, "Friedrich Wöhler and His American Pupils," *Journal of Chemical Education*, 21 (April, 1944), 158-70. Klooster and Shumway give a total of about 190 chemistry students at Göttingen in the period from 1850 to World War I; and I have multiplied this figure by a factor of five, which is approximately the proportion of American chemistry students in Germany who studied at Göttingen, according to a study of the biographies of 185 American chemists (active in the years 1825-1900) given in the *National Cyclopaedia of American Biography*. The factor of five also makes an allowance for the students who matriculated at several universities while in Germany.

2. Thwing, 140-41. Of the 185 chemists of the *National Cyclopaedia* survey, 68 matriculated at German universities. In order of their popularity, the favorite institutions of this group were the University of Berlin, the University of Göttingen, Heidelberg University, Leipsig University, and the Freiberg Mining Academy. Of the non-German universities, the University of Paris was the only one which attracted significant numbers of American chemists, and it ran behind Berlin, Göttingen, and Heidelberg in order of popularity.

3. The reader should understand that what applied to the student of chemistry in the matter of German education usually applied to others as well. This was certainly the case for the motivations behind German study, as it was for the influence of German education on American students. Chemistry students were no different from any other American students in their attitudes and reactions.

4. A. H. Baynes, "German Student Life," *Fraser's Magazine*, 104 (1881), 643.

14

a level of chemical education that no American institution could match. Some American chemists saw economic advantage in having this more advanced German training. In the early 1850's Benjamin Silliman, Jr., then professor of chemistry at the University of Louisville, advised a former pupil to study in Germany if he possibly could. A German education, Silliman told the younger man, would open to him "the best places in the country," and would "before you know it transmute the coppers in your breeches pocket into gold."[5] Serious students saw a chance for intellectual adventure in Germany. A period of German study offered the incomparable opportunity to work under such masters of chemistry as Friedrich Wöhler at Göttingen, Heinrich Rose at Berlin, August Kekulé at Bonn, Justus von Liebig at Giessen and later Munich, and Robert Bunsen at Heidelberg.

Whatever his reasons for going to Germany, the American student found there a totally new way of life. Living amid a culture much older than his own, he was especially charmed by the smaller university towns, such as Göttingen and Heidelberg, whose beautiful and accessible surroundings presented opportunities for pleasant evening walks and holiday excursions.[6]

If the physical environment pleased the American student, he had his reservations about German students. Their social groups, the exclusive *Korps* and *Burschenschaften,* seemed to exist for no other purpose than that of keeping alive the custom of dueling. Although German youths claimed their sword-play built manliness and self-reliance, Americans found it revolting.[7] The heavy tippling of German students, and the noisy ritual they made of it, seemed particularly wicked to those youthful Americans reared to look upon sobriety as a cardinal virtue.[8] One youth, venturing to Germany in the 1850's, nearly gave up hope of finding a companion who did not indulge in the evils of "tobacco and intoxi-

5. February 1, 1854, to W. H. Brewer, Yale Memorabilia Collection, Yale University Library.

6. Stephen M. Babcock, 19 May, 1878, to his mother, Box 2 of correspondence, Stephen M. Babcock Papers, Wisconsin Historical Society Library, Madison.

7. See Friedrich Paulsen, *The German Universities, Their Character and Historical Development* (New York, 1895), 189-98; James M. Hart, *German Universities: A Narrative of Personal Experience, Together With A Comparison of the German, English, and American Systems of Higher Education* (New York, 1874).

8. Harvey W. Wiley, *Autobiography* (Indianapolis, 1930), 137.

cating drinks, such as wine, lager beer, tea, [and] coffee."[9]

The American chemistry student's academic experience in Germany was no less new and strange to him. Until the mid-1870's the German university had no counterpart in the United States and was an institution which rested upon ideas largely unknown in American education. The first of these was the idea of *Lernfreiheit*, or freedom of learning. In a German university the student could select his faculty and lectures with complete freedom. As the university had no taste for forced instruction, he was also free to absent himself from his lectures if he so desired. Even in non-academic matters the university exercised no control over the student. There were no chapel services, the student could choose his own place of lodging, and he was answerable only to himself or to civil authorities for his conduct.[10]

The second foundation of the German university was the idea of *Lehrfreiheit*, or freedom of teaching. Every member of the faculty, whether an *Ordentlicher* (or full) professor, or a lowly, unsalaried *Privatdozent*, had the right to teach "what he chooses, as he chooses."[11] The major implication of *Lehrfreiheit* was freedom from state restraint, but the tradition of freedom of teaching ideally made it possible for instructors to compete for the students of established professors and served to bring forth the best from every lecturer.[12] The ultimate gainer was the student for he heard lectures that were fresh and original.[13]

The third component of the German concept of a university was the idea of original research, which colored every aspect of the academic routine. The research dissertation, above all else, decided the fate of the applicant for the *Privatdozent* position.[14] Academic ad-

9. Evan Pugh, October 31, 1953, to Mr. Editor, quoted in C. A. Browne, "The European Laboratory Experiences of an Early American Agricultural Chemist—Dr. Evan Pugh," *Journal of Chemical Education* 7 (1930), 500.

10. Paulsen, 201-11; Baynes, 630-32, 641.   11. Hart, 251.

12. Actually freedom from state restraint and competition among the faculty were the ideal situations, and were not always attained in actual practice. Prussia's 1819 Carlsbad Decrees and Bismarck's Kulturkampf of the 1870's might be cited as examples of state policies which led to limitation of academic freedom. Regarding intrafaculty competition, at some universities the *Privatdozent* did not encroach on a field already staked out by an instructor of a higher grade. See George Hempt, "Instruction in German and American Universities," *The Nation*, 50 (1890), 241-42.

13. Hart, 270-71.

14. United States Bureau of Education, *The University of Bonn* (Circular number 3, Washington, 1882), 27.

vancement hinged also on research ability.[15] As one American noted, no German teacher "contents himself with merely attending to his classes, and sitting down at ease after he has got them at work. He is studying constantly himself; making original investigations and publishing them to the world."[16]

The American student soon found that research was central to his activity in the German university. Mere acquaintance with a body of knowledge was not enough. If he did not undergo a "trial of his strength in independent research," no matter how diligently he attended lectures and studied textbooks, he failed to meet the German requirements.[17]

The first task of the student of chemistry was to master the methods of science; he then had to apply those methods to at least one of the unsolved problems in his field, pursuing it doggedly until he could say to himself that "there is now nobody in the whole world" who could "instruct him further on this matter."[18]

Evan Pugh was one of the thousand-odd American chemistry students who sought advanced training in German universities. Pugh, later president of the Pennsylvania Agriculture College (the forerunner of Pennsylvania State College), went to Germany in the middle 1850's. One of the laboratories in which he worked was that of Professor Friedrich Wöhler at Göttingen. Pugh, like all of Wöhler's students, greatly revered the homely, humble master of chemistry. "To no man living," he remarked, "does the science of chemistry owe as much for the facts it embraces as to Professor Wöhler." Yet one could not find a more unostentatious man. Wöhler's "goodness of . . . heart," Pugh said, even surpassed his "simplicity of manners." Wöhler took a deep interest in his students, spending almost his entire day going "amongst them with his old coat and little cap on," to check the progress of their research.[19] When a student's project bogged down, Wöhler was "a most splendid man to suggest courses that will probably lead to results."[20]

Professor Wöhler did everything possible to facilitate his students' research. All equipment and chemicals in the laboratory were at

15. Paulsen, 131; G. Stanley Hall, "Research the Vital Spirit of Teaching," *The Forum*, 17 (1894), 569.
16. Evan Pugh, October 31, 1853, to Mr. Editor, quoted in Browne, 500.
17. Paulsen, 199.
18. Evan Pugh, October 31, 1853, to Mr. Editor, quoted in Browne, 500.
19. Evan Pugh, c. 1855, to Mr. Editor, quoted in Browne, 505.
20. July 23, 1855, letter to S. W. Johnson, quoted in Browne, 504.

the student's disposal. When the pupil needed a special piece of apparatus made to order, the laboratory assistants fashioned it almost immediately. If a student broke a piece of apparatus by carelessness, he had to pay two-thirds of its value; but if "you break it by unforeseen . . . explosion," Pugh said, "you pay nothing." Once, an explosion during one of Pugh's experiments totally demolished the equipment he was using. The blast brought Wöhler in from his lecture to learn the cause. On hearing Pugh's account of the mishap, the professor concluded that such an explosion could have happened to him as well, so the laboratory had to pay.[21]

Pugh was "well satisfied" that he came to Wöhler's laboratory. The students were all advanced, and they worked with great seriousness of purpose. For "pure chemistry" Pugh found Göttingen "the place of places."[22] There was "no other laboratory," in Pugh's opinion, "where more work, *original* work, or at least work on rare organic and inorganic substances is done than just here."[23]

American scholars returned to the United States eager to impose the German research tradition on American scientific education. Such was the aim of George J. Brush, who returned to accept a post at the Yale Scientific School. Writing in 1855 to S. W. Johnson, who would join him at New Haven, Brush expressed confidence that "we shall be able to make things move when we return home. We'll see whether we cannot revive things and inspire some new life in the School."[24]

German-trained chemists who returned to the United States between the 1850's and the 1870's found few opportunities to translate their idealism into action. Many young enthusiasts had experiences similar to that of the Williams College chemistry professor who, upon petitioning the college president for a research laboratory, was told, "You will please keep in mind that this is a college and not a technical school. The students who come here are not to be trained as chemists or geologists or physicists. . . . The object aimed at is culture, not practical knowledge."[25] German-trained chemists found a larger provision for instruction in their field in

21. *Ibid.*
22. August 2, 1857, to S. W. Johnson, quoted in Browne, 510.
23. July 23, 1855, to S. W. Johnson, quoted in Browne, 504.
24. May 13, 1855, quoted in Elizabeth Osborne, *From the Letter Files of Samuel W. Johnson* (New York, 1918), 90.
25. Quoted in Frederick Getman, *The Life of Ira Remsen* (Easton, Pennsylvania, 1940), 42.

the scientific schools and departments, but these institutions were for the most part devoted to training practical chemists, not research men. According to Nicholas Murray Butler, the rapid growth of technical schools was the "main obstacle to the full establishment in America of the pursuit of science for its own sake."[26]

Although devotees of the German research idea had only a limited field of action, time worked in their favor. Each year brought to the United States a new crop of German-trained scholars who favored reform in American higher education. In 1875 Andrew Ten Brook, University of Michigan Librarian, surveyed the American educational scene with optimism. While noting that the United States was still without a true university, he felt that the time for the establishment of one was near at hand. "We have a few great schools," he said, "which have outgrown the rank of the college, and can at once be advanced to that of the university when their governing powers so determine." If just one institution made the movement toward advanced training and research, Ten Brook felt, "others will follow."[27]

A year after Ten Brook's remarks America's first university, in the German sense, made its appearance. Contrary to Ten Brook's expectations, it did not emerge in New Haven, Cambridge, or Ann Arbor. The distinction, instead, went to Baltimore. The Johns Hopkins University was able to play an innovating role in American higher education because its benefactor gave his money almost without condition, leaving the institution's future in the hands of a board of trustees. Those trustees, in turn, sought the counsel of a group of university presidents who were under heavy debt to Germany for their ideas on higher education. The most fertile piece of advice offered to the trustee group was the suggestion that they tender the presidency of the Johns Hopkins to Daniel Coit Gilman, then head of the University of California and formerly professor of political economy at the Sheffield Scientific School.

Gilman's response to the Hopkins offer foretold the course that the new university would take. He advised the trustees that if they intended to establish just "another college," their offer "would not interest him." On the other hand, if they wanted to establish a university which could bring together the best professors and the most advanced students, one which could "extend its influence . . .

26. Introduction to Paulsen, xxiii.
27. *American State Universities* (Cincinnati, 1875), 322-23.

throughout the land," he would readily accept the Hopkins presidency. The trustees assented to Gilman's terms, and the new president began at once the work of gathering his faculty. In his men he looked first and foremost for the ability to "pursue independent and original investigation."[28]

Gilman placed the chemistry department under the direction of a man ideally suited for the job of building a chemistry program on the German model. Ira Remsen was thoroughly exposed to German ideas and methods, having studied at Munich under Liebig and at Göttingen with Wöhler and his assistant, Rudolph Fittig. Moreover, he had already proven himself an able researcher by the time he came to Baltimore, having published ten papers while in Germany and an equal number afterwards in the United States. Harmon Morse, another Göttingen scholar, became Remsen's able assistant at the Johns Hopkins.[29]

Remsen devised a course of study which would "encourage the most advanced work," and would develop a "true spirit of investigation" in his students.[30] In lecture courses Remsen and his associates offered training in the fundamentals of chemistry, but they took care to remind students that textbooks were only to be used as guides to instruction. The student was to stay abreast of new developments reported in chemical journals. To make students aware of current research, Remsen held bi-weekly journal seminars at which students reported on recent publications. Besides serving to call the students' attention to important new research, these sessions sharpened their critical faculties and helped them to improve their writing ability.[31]

The central feature of Remsen's chemistry program was laboratory instruction. Its aim was to give the student "a thorough knowledge of the pure science of Chemistry, and its methods."[32] Before Remsen allowed students to undertake research projects they had to demonstrate an ability to handle basic experimental manipula-

28. Daniel Coit Gilman, *The Launching of a University* (New York, 1906), 37-43; see *ibid.*, 7, 27, 28.
29. Getman, 31; W. A. Noyes and J. F. Norris, "Ira Remsen," National Academy of Sciences, *Biographical Memoirs*, 14 (1932), 210-13, 230; The Johns Hopkins University, *Official Circulars* (number 5, September, 1876), 1-3; Ira Remsen, "Harmon N. Morse," National Academy, *Memoirs*, 21 (1926), 1-2.
30. Johns Hopkins University, *Official Circulars* (no. 8, April, 1877), 3.
31. Getman, 55-56.
32. Johns Hopkins Circulars (no. 8, April, 1877), 3.

20

tions. Scholars quickly learned that Remsen and Morse were sticklers for thoroughness. One student, determined to get the preliminary work behind him as quickly as possible, hastily ran an analysis and took his findings to Morse for approval. Then came the rude awakening: Morse, the "big, kindly soft-spoken man . . . gave me to understand very gently but very firmly that approximate results did not suffice—I was to do the work over and over again until exact and consistent findings were obtained." [33]

After proving his familiarity with basic procedure, the Hopkins student had the opportunity of performing an investigation. Remsen set high standards for this work. He let the student know that he would not accept as a research dissertation "a mere compilation, such as could be worked up in a good library." What Remsen wanted was "a discussion of some problem on the basis of experiments undertaken by the candidate for the purpose." [34]

Little applied research came out of Remsen's laboratory. He felt that investigation in pure chemistry, no matter how remote, was the best basis of preparation, whether "the student has in view a practical or a scientific object." [35] Hopkins students found everything they needed to facilitate their experimentation: technical journals, special equipment, and experienced counsel. But Remsen and Morse did not spoon-feed their pupils. Aiming to build self-reliance in their scholars, the two professionals, after outlining each research problem thoroughly, left the budding investigators pretty much to their own devices. [36]

Remsen's success in building a chemistry department which could turn advanced scholars into independent investigators was representative of the success of other Hopkins professors. The collective achievement of such men as Ira Remsen in chemistry, Henry Rowland in physics, Basil Gildersleeve in Greek, J. J. Sylvester in mathematics, and Herbert Baxter Adams in history came to be known as "the Hopkins example"; in the 1880's and 1890's this example carried the American graduate school experiment to completion. In those two decades old and new institutions alike organized formal departments of graduate instruction patterned after the John Hopkins University. In 1882 Yale College organized a graduate department, and five years later the University of Penn-

33. Statement of Dr. W. H. Howell, quoted in Remsen, 9.
34. Johns Hopkins Circulars (no. 8, April, 1877), 3.
35. *Ibid.*   36. *Ibid.*, 2, 4; Getman, 69.

sylvania made its philosophy department a separate graduate school. Before the close of the century many state institutions, such as the universities of Michigan and Wisconsin, likewise set up departments of graduate instruction.[37]

While the graduate school movement was in progress, American chemistry students continued to seek advanced training in Germany. But the American university Ph.D. was so gaining in prestige that in the last decade of the century at least as many American chemists took theirs at such institutions as the Johns Hopkins, Yale, Harvard, Michigan, Columbia, and Chicago as earned the degree in the universities of Germany.[38] In 1905 a policy decision of the University of Berlin ended the qualitative distinction between German and American education in chemistry. In that year the Berlin faculty announced that graduate work in chemistry, or in any other field, done in member institutions of the Association of American Universities, would be accepted as equal to work done in residence in any German university.[39] By the turn of this century American chemists had a system of education equal to any in the world. Not only did this system disseminate existing knowledge; it also trained American workers to add to that body of knowledge.

37. See Frederick Rudolph, *The American College and University* (New York, 1962), 335; Edward Potts Cheyney, *History of the University of Pennsylvania* (Philadelphia, 1940), 296-98; Thomas Jefferson Wertenbaker, *Princeton, 1746-1896* (Princeton, 1946), 379.

38. In 1900 the American Chemical Society polled the small colleges to find out how many of their students still sought advanced training from German universities. The results of the poll showed that students invariably took their graduate training in the large American universities (American Chemical Society, *Twenty-fifth Anniversary of the American Chemical Society* [Easton, Pennsylvania, 1902], 135-36). The Survey of American chemists in the *National Cyclopaedia* showed that of the chemists who took their graduate training either in Germany or America (but not in both places) in the 1880's, the German-trained students exceeded the American-trained students by nine to five; in the 1890's, however, the lead was reversed, with the American-trained students outnumbering those trained in Germany by eight to five.

39. "An Educational Entente," *The Nation*, 80 (1905), 185.

3. PROFESSIONAL ORGANIZATION: THE NATIONAL SOCIETIES

Prior to the middle 1870's American chemists had no national organization of their own, nor had any attempt been made to establish one. Many societies, such as the American Association for the Advancement of Science, existed in support of science in general, and within such groups there were places for chemistry. But chemists were ready for a professional home of their own: the number of practitioners of the science was increasing rapidly; chemistry was an academic specialty in leading institutions of higher learning; and chemists recognized special needs and problems.[1]

American professionals saw much to be gained from having their own national organization. Such a body could organize the manpower required to solve many technical problems in the science, and the adoption of changes in chemical practice by a national society would carry enough weight to gain the acceptance of all practitioners. In the 1870's American workers lacked a system for indexing the literature. There was no uniformity in analytical methods, and the absence of exactness in atomic weight standards especially plagued chemists. A national organization offered the hope of solving each of those problems.

Chemists eager to build their profession on the German model also saw in a national society a means of widening their field of influence. National meetings would give leaders an opportunity to make the teaching of chemistry more uniform, to stimulate the research of less active workers, and generally to impose higher standards of performance on the whole body of American chemists.

Chemists took the first steps toward organizing their science in the early 1870's. In 1873 at the close of the American Association meeting, a small group of men, including Frank Clarke of Cincinnati University and Harvey W. Wiley of Northwestern Christian University (later Butler University), met to consider a separate organization for chemistry within the association. At that time the association mixed chemists with astronomers, mathematicians, and physicists, and the hectic schedule of the annual gathering gave chemists no time to meet separately. To remedy that situation Clarke, Wiley, and other conferees drafted a petition, calling

1. American Chemical Society, *Twenty-fifth Anniversary of the American Chemical Society* (Easton, Pennsylvania, 1902), 25-33.

on the 1874 session to create a permanent section of chemistry.[2]

Prior to the 1874 association meeting, another event took place which was significant in the establishment of a national organization. In early August chemists gathered to celebrate what they called the Centennial of Chemistry. The idea originated with Henry C. Bolton, professor at the Columbia School of Mines. In an open letter to the *American Chemist,* Bolton reminded his associates that 1774, the year of Priestley's discovery of oxygen, marked the birthdate of modern chemistry. Would it not, Bolton asked, "be an agreeable event if American chemists should meet on the first day of August, 1874, at some pleasant watering place to discuss chemical questions, especially the wonderfully rapid progress of chemical science in the past hundred years?" Professionals concurred that it would be agreeable, and the Centennial was a huge success. Scientists from fifteen states and Canada met and heard addresses on the progress of chemistry and the contributions of American workers.

The enthusiasm engendered during that first nation-wide conference of chemists led to a discussion of ways to continue the spirit of the Centennial. At that point the idea of an independent national chemical society made its first appearance. Although Centennial president Charles F. Chandler, editor of the *American Chemist,* supported the suggestion, the idea met strong opposition. The very size of the country, the wide dispersion of chemists, and the lack of any professional identity among them, opponents of the idea argued, would stunt the growth of an independent society. After an earnest debate the Centennial delegates decided to drop the idea of independent organization and endorse the plan for a section of chemistry within the American Association.[3]

Two weeks later the association convened. Strengthened by support from the Centennial, the petition for a separate organization of chemistry won the approval of the association's standing committee, and in the section of "Chemistry, Chemical Physics, Chemical Technology, Mineralogy, and Metallurgy," American workers had their first national body.[4]

2. *Ibid.,* 87; Wiley, *Autobiography* (Indianapolis, 1930), 217.

3. Benjamin Silliman, Jr., "American Contributions to Chemistry," *The American Chemist,* 5 (1875), 70-114; see *ibid.,* 195-209, 327-28; "Centennial of Chemistry," *ibid.,* 37-38, 41.

4. H. C. Bolton, "Address," *Proceedings of the American Association for the Advancement of Science,* 31 (1883), 229-55. E. F. Smith, *Chemistry in*

Although it suffered an initial rejection, the idea of an independent national society retained its vitality beyond the Centennial. C. F. Chandler and a group of New York City chemists continued interested in a separate society, and in January, 1876, they circulated a letter among professionals calling for a city-wide association "which would lead to a better understanding and a closer acquaintance among its members."[5]

The response to the January letter was so heartening that the New York City organizers decided to broaden their plan and call for the establishment of a national body. Accordingly, in March, 1876, a second letter went forth to chemists in all parts of the United States. In that circular Chandler stated in clear terms the benefits to be gained from independent national organization: such action, he said, "would prove a powerful and healthy stimulus to original research among us, and . . . would awaken and develop much talent now wasting in isolation, besides bringing the members of the association into closer union, and ensuring a better appreciation of our science and its students on the part of the general public."[6] Within two weeks chemists from seventeen states registered enthusiastic support of the idea. On the strength of that response the committee called an organizational meeting, and a motion creating the American Chemical Society passed with but a few dissenting votes.[7]

The optimism of the organizational meeting continued into succeeding months. One by one the leading names in American chemistry appeared on the society's rolls. The chemical society also attracted such vigorous young professionals as Harvey Wiley, Frank Clarke, and Ira Remsen. By 1877 the society was meeting monthly, publishing its proceedings, and showing its intention to be an active professional force. Despite the doubts registered at the Centennial, the nation's chemists gave every indication that they did not need the shelter of an established association. They could support their own society.[8]

America (New York, 1914), 78, 246-52; C. A. Browne, "History of Chemical Education," 1820-1870," *Journal of Chemical Education,* 9 (1932), 9, 718; "Scientific Intelligence," *American Journal of Science,* 9 (1875), 397.

5. C. F. Chandler, *et al.,* "Letter of January 22, 1876," *Proceedings of the American Chemical Society,* 1 (1877), 5.

6. Chandler, *et al.,* "Letter of March 22, 1876," 5-6.

7. "April Meeting of the ACS," *Proceedings, ACS,* 1 (1877), 7-8, 9-13.

8. ACS, *25th Anniversary,* 45-57; *Proceedings ACS,* 1 (1877), 1-252.

In the ten years between 1877 and 1887, the chemical section of the American Association for the Advancement of Science prospered. Meeting separately during annual association gatherings, chemists had a chance to concentrate on the work of their discipline. The migratory meetings of the association brought workers from nearly all areas of the nation together within the chemistry section and enabled individuals to see their work as a part of a national effort. Within the first decade after its establishment, the section became a leading voice in professional matters.[9]

By contrast, the first decade of the American Chemical Society was a dismal one. After its strong start the society began to stumble. Influential chemists working outside the New York City area began to lose interest and leave the society. In 1877 Frank Clarke resigned, just two months after joining. By 1881 Remsen and Wiley had withdrawn.[10] A chief reason for their desertion was the increasing local orientation: the society was becoming more and more a New York City club, controlled by local members and existing only for their benefit. Although its organizers promised at least one meeting per year outside the city, the pledge was soon forgotten.[11] Harvey Wiley summed up the dissatisfaction of non-New York chemists: the sole benefit he received from the society, he said, was simply a receipt for his annual dues.[12]

Dissatisfaction with the official publication of the society was an added reason for its decline. In 1879 the *Journal of the American Chemical Society* appeared, filling the void left by the discontinuance of C. F. Chandler's *American Chemist*. The *Journal*, however, was an inferior substitute.[13] This was largely because of the financial problems of the society. In 1880 the editor issued a statement to all subscribers announcing the interruption of monthly publication because of "failure of members to pay promptly their annual dues."

9. ACS, *25th Anniversary*, 86-98; *Proceedings AAAS*, 25-37 (1876-1888).

10. Charles Albert Browne, and Mary Elvira Weeks, *A History of the American Chemical Society* (Washington, 1952), 27; George F. Barker, "Address," *Proceedings AAAS*, 25 (1877), 86; *Proceedings ACS*, 1 (1879-80), 1; "Proceedings of the ACS," *Journal of the American Chemical Society*, 3 (1881), 1.

11. Chandler, *et al.*, "Letter, March 22, 1876," *Proceedings ACS*, 1 (1877), 6.

12. "Proceedings of the Association of Official Agricultural Chemists," *Division of Chemistry, United States Department of Agriculture* (Bulletin 24, 1890), 66.

13. Browne, "Chemical Society of Washington," *Journal of the Washington Academy*, 28 (1938), 235-37.

Henceforth, he said, "the *Journal* will appear at such intervals as papers received and funds on hand will warrant."[14]

The appearance of splinter organizations confirmed the fact that the society's authority was fading. The Chemical Society of Washington, founded in 1884 and made up of capital city professionals, was one such group. The appeal of the New York society was so weak in Washington that by 1887 every American Chemical Society member in that city resigned and joined the local body.[15] By the end of the 1880's, society influence was at its lowest ebb. Even staunch New York City supporters had to face the obvious: their organization had no valid claim to the title of national spokesman. The plans of the founders to make the society an instrument of national unity seemed impossible to fulfill.

In the midst of that disintegration, however, a movement was afoot to convert the American Chemical Society into a truly national body. By 1888 a group of chemists within the American Association were giving another look at the idea of an independent national organization. Although pleased with their representation within the association, those professionals saw simply that chemistry was outgrowing it. By the late 1880's there were well over 2,000 chemists in the country, and yet only 200 of them maintained active membership in the American Association.[16] Though influential in the profession, the association section was not inspiring the active participation of rank-and-file chemists. Nor was it likely to do so, being a noncontinuing organization which gathered once a year for a week's meeting and then disbanded. What the reforming chemists wanted was an active society whose organization enabled it to tap the interest of every worker in America.

Unlike the first effort to establish an independent national society, the second was an unqualified success, due chiefly to the persistence, strategy, and tact of two Washington, D. C., professionals, Frank Clarke (then with the Geological Survey) and Harvey Wiley (of the Department of Agriculture). Quite a strange-

14. "Notice," *Journal ACS*, 1-2 (1879-80), back leaf.
15. Browne, "Dr. Thomas Antisell and his Associates in the Founding of the Chemical Society of Washington," *Journal of the Washington Academy*, 28 (1938), 223-25; Browne, "Chemical Society of Washington," 236.
16. "Proceedings AOAC," *Division of Chemistry, Bulletin* 24 (1890), 67; Browne, "Chemical Society of Washington," *Journal of the Washington Academy*, 28 (1938), 240-41. The 1880 census listed a total of 2,000 chemists in the country, according to Clarke in his address before the AOAC.

looking team was this Clarke-Wiley combination. Wiley, a giant hulk of a man, possessed the brash self-confidence of one who thrived on controversy. His reputation for dramatic utterance and his prodigious appetite—a ten-course meal gave him no difficulty— were legendary in Washington. Wiley used to claim he was like the moon: "the fuller I am the brighter I shine." The chemical group in the Department of Agriculture was devoted to its chief. As one associate put it, Wiley commanded loyalty by the "sheer force of a marvelous personality."[17] Clarke, by contrast, attracted no attention by his girth. He was thinly framed and little more than five feet tall. His quiet, retiring manner seldom made him the center of attention, and associates remembered that even his laugh was subdued: "A sort of hissing snicker was the best he could manage." If Clarke was popular with those who worked for him, this was not so because he conquered his co-workers, but because he left them alone.[18] Both he and Wiley, however, possessed equal measures of organizational talent, as was demonstrated by their maneuvers to establish a strong national society for their profession.

By 1889 American chemists were generally willing to make another attempt at forming a national society. The big obstacle was finding the right basis for organization. In an attempt to solve that problem the American Association chemists asked Clarke to head a group to study possible plans for a new society. Already serving as chairman of a similar committee within the Chemical Society of Washington, Clarke had considered the subject of organization thoroughly and had a definite plan in mind. His position as spokesman for two of the most influential chemistry groups gave him the authority to gain a hearing for his scheme.[19]

Clarke had conferred with Wiley on his plan of organization and the two were in close agreement, deciding that the first step should be the introduction of the plan at some professional gathering. On that matter Wiley was in a position to help. In early fall, 1889, the Association of Official Agricultural Chemists was to hold its annual meeting. That large body of state, federal, and university chemists also had a committee on a new chemical society, and

17. W. W. Skinner, *et al.*, "Obituary on H. W. Wiley," *Journal of the Association of Official Agricultural Chemists*, 14 (February 15, 1931), xvii.
18. Albert A. Martin, "The Great Analysis," *The Capital Chemist*, 3 (April, 1953), 113.
19. "Report of the Committee of Conference on Organization of a National Chemical Society," *Proceedings AAAS*, 38 (1890), 35-38; 39 (1891), 139.

Wiley was its chairman. It was an easy matter for him to arrange Clarke's appearance on the program.

What American chemists needed, Clarke told the agricultural group, was an organization patterned after the British Society of Chemical Industry. Established in 1881, that society was a federation of active local chemical groups, each established in a major industrial center. The federal scheme, Clarke asserted, prevented concentration of control in one locale, which characterized the American Chemical Society. Not only did the United States have enough chemical centers to support local sections, but the vastness of this country made the British plan especially suitable. "By such a system," he explained, "every member of the Society could be within comparatively easy reach of some one section, while at the same time all would be likely to get the worth of their subscription fees in a journal which should be a common medium for all."[20]

After the plan was in the open, Clarke and Wiley tried to get tangible expressions of support for their scheme. If they could maneuver the issue of organization into channels of their own choosing, any fight that might develop over a new association would center around their plan and not some other. Seizing the initiative, they drafted a circular, outlining their concept for a new organization (which they named the Continental Chemical Society) and sent it to chemists all over the country, with requests for their opinions on it.[21]

When the replies began to come in, the two Washington chemists were gratified to see an overwhelming vote of approval for the Contiential Society idea. They planned to use the replies to force the American Chemical Society to step aside for the creation of the new national body. By the summer of 1890, however, the American Chemical Society had done the unexpected. Fearing that Clarke and Wiley's efforts would put an end to their work to build a national society, the New York City chemists reshaped their constitution to provide for local sections and migratory annual meetings. In an attempt to head off the establishment of a new association, the society had turned itself into a group that closely resembled the one for which the reformers were calling.[22]

20. "Proceedings AOAC," *Division of Chemistry Bulletin* 24 (1890), 67-68.
21. "Report of the Committee of Conference on Organization of a National Chemical Society," *Proceedings AAAS*, 39 (1891), 139-42.
22. "Fellows of the AAAS," *Proceedings AAAS*, 39 (1891), lxxvi; Browne and Weeks, *American Chemical Society,* 453.

Clarke and Wiley saw that they must give recognition to the New York group's attempts at reform, for disregarding the society's claims to be the national spokesman would only create bitterness that would hamper a new association. Accordingly, they sought to arrange a compromise with the New York body. From August, 1890, to August, 1891, they met with agents of the New York group as well as with committees of the other chemical organizations.[23] Finally, in August, 1891, the conferees reached a settlement. The New York chemists agreed to yield all claims of national authority and to reorganize themselves as a local section of the new society. In return, the new organization would retain the name of the old and continue its journal.[24] Representative of the new unity among American chemists was the election of Harvey Wiley as first president of the revitalized American Chemical Society.[25]

By the end of the century the society was fulfilling every expectation. Some 1,700 chemists held membership in 13 local sections. The sections met monthly and the national body twice a year. In a 1901 appraisal of the society, its secretary said that the combination of local and general meetings gave members not only "an opportunity of close personal acquaintance with one another, and a better knowledge of the work done by the great body of chemists," but also "a keener insight into the Science of Chemistry and the best means of advancing it."[26]

Although the firm establishment of an independent society of chemists had to await the 1890's, the nation's professionals reaped the benefits of organization even while they were seeking a better form of association. Their American Association section, especially, enabled chemists to establish those personal contacts which so stimulated their professional efforts. Meetings facilitated an exchange of ideas and techniques which provided chemists with fresh insights into their work. Each man became more closely acquainted with others in his field, and with this closer accord came the desire

23. "Report of the Committee of Conference on Organization of a National Chemical Society," *Proceedings AAAS*, 39 (1891), 140; also see 139; "The Philadelphia General Meeting," *Journal ACS*, 12 (1890), 80.

24. "The Philadelphia General Meeting," *Journal ACS*, 13 (1891), 8; Browne, "Chemical Society of Washington," *Journal of the Washington Academy*, 28 (1938), 240.

25. "Proceedings ACS," *Journal ACS*, 13 (1891), 227; 14 (1892), 311; Browne and Weeks, *American Chemical Society*, 38, 58.

26. "Report of the General Secretary of the ACS, 1901," quoted in Browne and Weeks, *American Chemical Society*, 63.

to maintain the respect of one's fellows. Knowing that shoddy performance would bring the disfavor of associates, each member spurred himself to produce his best work.

Meetings also gave chemists the chance to make a united attack on the technical problems in their science. In 1882 Professor H. C. Bolton called his American Association colleagues' attention to the need for an index of chemical literature. The growth of modern chemistry, said Bolton, had brought such a multiplication of special treatises that "mere acquaintance with their titles becomes a serious undertaking for busy workers in the laboratory." Having to search for a particular point "throughout the maze of modern chemical journals, transactions, treatises, and hand books," was both time-consuming and frustrating for the researcher.[27] Following Bolton's suggestion, association chemists named an indexing committee, which by 1900 was providing guides to the whole range of chemical literature.[28]

The national organizations gave continuing attention to the problem of standardizing analytical methods. The Association of Agricultural Chemists concentrated on bringing uniformity and accuracy into the field of fertilizer analysis.[29] In 1889 the American Association section participated in an international effort to set standards for iron and steel analysis, and in 1891 the American Chemical Society sought a uniform test for water hardness.[30]

Professional organization was responsible, too, for reforms in atomic weights. In 1893 the American Chemical Society asked Frank Clarke to head a committee charged with the responsibility of reviewing annually all the atomic weight research done by the world's chemists. As a result of the committee's work, the society was able to publish each year a revised atomic weight table, which significantly aided the advance of chemical science.[31]

The national societies provided a forum from which the most in-

27. H. C. Bolton, "Address," *Proceedings AAAS*, 31 (1883), 249-50.

28. "Report of the Committee on Indexing the Chemical Literature," *Proceedings AAAS*, 31-39 (1883-91); "Scientific Intelligence," *American Journal of Science*, 29 (1885), 61-62.

29. "Proceedings AOAC," *Division of Chemistry Bulletin* 7 (1885), 49.

30. J. W. Langley, "International Standards for the Analysis of Iron and Steel," *Proceedings AAAS*, 38 (1890), 185; "Proceedings ACS," *Journal ACS*, 13 (1891), 109-10.

31. F. W. Clarke, "Report of the Committee on Determinations of Atomic Weight, Published During 1893," *Journal ACS*, 16 (1894), 193. See also 179-93.

fluential and talented professionals sought to impose their patterns of work on less able or less experienced members. Leading workers urged their associates to give closer attention to published literature. At the 1879 American Association meeting Ira Remsen charged that American chemists too often tried to blame poor research records on inadequate apparatus or burdensome teaching loads. The real reason for substandard performance was that they were too lazy to read the literature.[32] In 1893 Albert Prescott, University of Michigan chemist, reminded his American Chemical Society colleagues that a researcher could not even begin an original investigation without knowing the literature, for he would have no way of determining at what point the last researcher stopped.[33]

Teaching standards came out of the interchange of the national professional meetings. In the 1880's, American Association chemists held several sessions on instructional methods. Frank Clarke, Ira Remsen, and Benjamin Silliman, Jr., participated in one teaching seminar which discussed, among other things, the educational benefits of laboratory work and its proper relation to the chemistry lecture. In the 1890's, the association section created a regular session of "Didactic Chemistry," in which leading members read papers describing their methods of teaching a certain concept or branch of chemistry. The long-term effect of such discussions was to standardize and, at the same time, upgrade the teaching of chemistry in the United States.[34]

National society meetings served as a clearinghouse for American research, for leading workers used the gatherings to give direction to the research effort of their colleagues. In 1877, at the inaugural session of the American Chemical Society, its president, New York University chemist John W. Draper, called for increased study of the spatial arrangement of atoms in chemical compounds and reminded his associates that the "geometry of chemistry was that of three dimensions, not of two."[35] The next year Frank Clarke criticized American Association chemists for giving too much time to the static side of chemistry, synthesis and structure of compounds. Urging more investigation of phenomena occurring during reaction,

32. "Address," *Proceedings AAAS*, 28 (1879), 213-18.
33. "The Immediate Work in Chemical Science," *Proceedings AAAS*, 41 (1893), 1-6.
34. "Proceedings of the Section of Chemistry of the AAAS," *Science*, 4 (1884), 321-22; "Contents," *Proceedings AAAS*, 44 (1896), v-vi.
35. "Science in America," *Proceedings, ACS*, 1 (1877) 144.

Clarke said that chemistry's greatest need was not for more un-related data but for a grand theory that would relate existing information. To prepare to search for that theory, chemists should immediately begin to calculate the physical constants of nature (densities, boiling points, etc.).[36] In 1882 J. W. Langley, University of Michigan Professor, reinforced Clarke's message. Chemistry had produced many branches, Langley held, but few grand hypotheses which had stood the test of time. The science needed more work on the dynamics of chemical reactions, and the Michigan professor specifically urged his American Association colleagues to investigate speeds of reactions.[37]

In the very nature of the projects suggested by the leading chemists there was the implication of a standard for American research. In all their recommendations, leading professionals made no effort to guide American chemists toward investigations of an immediate practical use. Rather, they recommended work on the spatial arrangement of atoms, chemical constants, and reaction speeds, all in the realm of basic research.

36. "Address," *Proceedings AAAS*, 28 (1879), 131-33.
37. "Address," *Proceedings AAAS*, 33 (1884), 141-59.

4. PROFESSIONAL ORGANIZATION: NATIONAL JOURNALS

In 1818, in the first volume of his *American Journal of Science,* Benjamin Silliman, Sr., of Yale wrote that "In every enlightened country, men illustrious for talent, worth, and knowledge, are ardently engaged in enlarging the boundaries of natural science; and the history of their labors and discoveries is communicated to the world chiefly through the medium of scientific journals. The utility of such journals has become generally evident; they are the heralds of science; they proclaim its toils and its achievements; they demonstrate its intimate connection with the comfort, as with the intellectual and moral improvement of our species; and they often procure for it enviable honors and substantial rewards."[1] Silliman was one of the first American chemists to perceive the importance of publication media to the development of his profession, and in the years from its founding through the 1860's Silliman's *Journal* was the chief spokesman for chemistry in America.

The *Journal* served all the sciences, from anthropology to zoology. Though Silliman could devote only a portion of his pages to any single field, the *Journal* promoted the interests of chemistry in many ways. It brought a measure of public notice and recognition to the efforts of American workers. Until the 1870's the *Journal* was the major avenue of publication for active American chemists.[2] Accepting only those applied and basic researches of high quality, Silliman's periodical imposed a standard of competence on American investigation, and by its regularity of issue American professionals had the assurance that their researches would secure proper credit in matters of priority.

Harvard zoologist Louis Agassiz correctly described Silliman's

1. "Introduction," *American Journal of Science,* 1 (1818), 1.
2. In the third quarter of the nineteenth century the small group of American researchers was led by such men as J. Lawrence Smith, Wolcott Gibbs, M. Carey Lea, T. Sterry Hunt, Josiah P. Cooke, Eben Horsford, and John W. Mallett. All these chemists, except Cooke, relied more heavily on the *American Journal of Science and Arts* than any other publication, European or American, as a vehicle for getting their researches into print. For evidence of this reliance on the New Haven *Journal,* see the National Academy of Sciences, *Biographical Memoirs,* 2 (1886), 239-48, for Smith; 7 (1913), 19-22, for Gibbs; 5 (1905), 204-8, for Lea; 15 (1934), 221-37, for Hunt; 4 (1902), 181-82, for Cooke. For Horsford and Mallett, see Benjamin Silliman, Jr., "American Contributions to Chemistry," *American Chemist,* 5 (1875), 107.

Journal as the main channel through which European research reached the New World.[3] But Agassiz was only half right. The channel carried information eastward as well: going to libraries in England, France, and Germany, the New Haven periodical kept foreign workers appraised of American investigations in chemistry and every other science.

Silliman's *Journal* was not the only American publication whose pages were open to the chemical researcher. In the 1850's and 1860's many other general science publications, such as the *Journal of the Franklin Institute,* gave some notice to chemical investigation.[4] None of the others, however, featured it as did Silliman's periodical. Researches also appeared in journals not primarily devoted to science. In 1848 Samuel W. Johnson, soon to be at Sheffield Scientific School, published an article in the agricultural organ, *Cultivator.* Some ten years later Charles F. Chandler placed his report on alcohol fermentation in a most unlikely journal, the magazine *Biblical Temperance.*[5]

Prior to the 1870's the only purely chemical journals were those published in Europe; among them, German periodicals occupied the front rank. American chemistry students attending the German universities in the 1850's and 1860's saw at first hand the close connection between periodicals and German pre-eminence in chemical research. Their plan to reform chemistry in the United States along German lines included a wish to have American journals equal in quality to the German periodicals. But desire alone was not enough to effect the transformation, and their early inability to carry out reforms sorely frustrated the German-trained students. In 1857 Samuel Johnson of the Yale Scientific School wanted to know what was "the matter, that with all our enterprise and reputed keenness in foreseeing every event that promises profit, we allow the slow Old World to keep out of sight ahead of us on this track [toward original research]."[6]

3. Elizabeth Cary Agassiz, *Louis Agassiz, His Life and Correspondence* (2 volumes, Boston, 1886), 2:413-14.

4. For a survey of the place of publication for American chemical research prior to 1874, see Silliman, Jr., 70-114.

5. T. B. Osborne, "Samuel W. Johnson," National Academy of Sciences, *Biographical Memoirs,* 7 (1913), 216; M. T. Bogert, "Charles F. Chandler," National Academy of Sciences, *Biographical Memoirs,* 14 (1932), 179.

6. From an editorial by Johnson in *Country Gentleman;* quoted in Elizabeth A. Osborne, *From the Letter Files of Samuel W. Johnson* (New Haven, 1918), 118.

American chemists could not hope to have chemical journals equal to those of Germany, however, until the American profession underwent other changes. Scientific publication media were intimately tied to general progress in science and could not precede it. Journals, once established, were the instigators of scientific advance, but their establishment was also the result of this advance. The appearance of chemical journals had to await, for one thing, a greater degree of specialization among practitioners. Until there was a body of workers who thought of themselves as chemists, rather than jack-of-all-trades scientists, a chemical journal could not command strong support. Furthermore, a journal could not thrive in an educational system that gave no encouragement to chemical work. Until American chemists had the facilities and opportunities to engage in research, they could not make contributions sufficient to fill the pages of a journal. In the 1850's and 1860's a publication of general scientific interest, such as Silliman's *Journal*, was not only all American chemists needed; it was all they could hope to have.

But American chemistry was not standing still. In the 1850's and 1860's the scientific school movement was gaining momentum, bringing greater opportunities for specialization and better facilities for original work. One of the by-products of the movement was America's first bona fide chemical journal, *The American Chemist*. First appearing in 1870, its editors were brothers Charles F. and William H. Chandler. Both Chandlers were connected with scientific schools—Charles with the Columbia College School of Mines, and William with the science department of Lehigh University.

In announcing their publication the editors informed readers that the *American Chemist* would serve both those workers engaged in theoretical investigations and those devoted to applied chemistry. The Chandlers also announced their determination to expose "humbug" and "fraud" whenever they appeared in the "guise of science." Speaking directly to American manufacturers, the editors cautioned that hostility to science could only hurt industrial interests, because the time was fast approaching when industry would have to "invoke the aid of science." Concluding their announcement, the Chandlers appealed for manufacturers' support and expressed the hope that "intimate relations may be established between them and the scientific men who are capable of improving their respective arts."[7]

7. "Announcement," *American Chemist*, 1 (1871), 1.

The publication emphasized applied chemistry. Representative contributions were those of William H. Chandler on commercial production of bromine and iodine and of T. Sterry Hunt, Canadian Geological Survey chemist, on the process of extracting copper from its ores.[8] *The American Chemist* did not exclude theoretical material, however: the first volume contained a study of molecular classification and a discussion of a new method for determining alkali metals in silicates.[9]

Although not as strong a force for the promotion of basic research as was Silliman's *Journal,* the *American Chemist* encouraged professional interests more effectively than the general science journals in other ways. The Chandlers were quick to defend American chemists in the face of any challenge. In 1870, when the California State University dismissed a professor of chemistry without offering him a bill of particulars, the *American Chemist* castigated the university's trustees and charged that not even a "mill-owner in New England would discharge his operatives without an explanation of the cause of his actions."[10] A year later when President Eliot of Harvard discontinued advanced training in chemistry at the Lawrence Scientific School, the Chandlers went into action again, expressing great pain over Eliot's decision. "We trust," said the editors, that "no personal motives have influenced this decision," but declared themselves at a loss to account "for this retrograde movement of Harvard."[11]

The *American Chemist* gave strong support to the budding movement to establish an organization of chemists. In 1874, when the idea of a Centennial of Chemistry was being discussed, the *Ameri-*

8. "The Production of Iodine and Bromine," *ibid.,* 47-49; "Notes on . . . the Process for Extraction of Copper from its Ores," *ibid.,* 199-200. A large number of the articles in the *American Chemist* were reprints of ones which appeared originally in the British publication, *Chemical News.* The *American Chemist* had replaced an American supplement to the *Chemical News,* buying its stock and subscription list; and throughout its existence, the *American Chemist* relied on the *Chemical News* for a goodly portion of its material.

9. George F. Barker, "On Molecular Classification," *ibid.,* 359-60; J. Lawrence Smith, "Determination of Alkalies in Silicates by Ignition with Carbonate of Lime and Sal Ammoniac," *ibid.,* 404-7.

10. "The California State University," *ibid.,* 224-25.

11. "The Lawrence Scientific School," *ibid.,* 430. Some chemists speculated that Eliot was acting on an old grudge when he took Gibbs' duties in chemistry away from him. In 1863 Eliot had hoped for the post of Rumford Professor at the Lawrence Scientific School, but Harvard had passed Eliot by and chose Gibbs to fill the post. Shortly after, Eliot resigned his Harvard tutorship in chemistry, not to return until 1869, when he came back as president.

can Chemist gave it every encouragement. Following the gathering, the Chandlers published a full account of the Centennial, including the proceedings of each meeting and all major addresses.[12]

Although the *American Chemist* served the interests of chemists very commendably, it failed to establish that rapport with American industry which its editors saw as essential to its financial stability. In 1877, after several years of operating at a loss, the Chandlers had to give up their enterprise.[13] Ironically, American manufacturers, whose demands for a more practical education indirectly produced the journal, turned their backs on the *American Chemist*. In the 1870's American industry, while demanding changes in education, was not yet ready to accept chemistry, chemists, or chemical publications as being essential to successful operation.

In 1877 American chemists were once again without a specialized journal. A decade earlier the absence of such a publication was not critical, because workers found the general science periodicals adequate to their needs. By 1877, however, with the increase in research, general science journals no longer sufficed. In 1878 Frank Clarke spoke to his American Association colleagues about the problem of publications. American research, he said, was proliferating, but "how is all this material published? A little of it in the *American Journal of Science and Arts;* a part in foreign periodicals; another portion in several local transactions. . . . In short the work is widely scattered; and some of it is effectually buried beyond the reach of a majority of our fellow chemists." To bring this research together, to stimulate inactive chemists, and to give the world a truer picture of American standing in chemistry, professionals needed a specialized journal. A new publication, Clarke urged, must "take root somewhere, and that without much delay."[14]

In 1879 Clarke's suggestions bore fruit in the establishment of two new professional journals. One of them, however, had a troubled career. Although the American Chemical Society intended its *Journal* to be a medium of communication for all the nation's workers, a year after the appearance of the first issue its editor had to suspend publication temporarily for want of sufficient funds and articles.[15]

12. "Centennial of Chemistry," *American Chemist*, 4 (1874), 362; 5 (1875), 35-114, 195-209, 327-28.
13. "Sketch of C. F. Chandler," *Popular Science Monthly*, 16 (1880), 841.
14. "Address," *Proceedings AAAS*, 27 (1879), 141.
15. "Notice," *Journal ACS*, 1-2 (1879-80), back leaf.

Throughout the 1880's problems of irregular publication continued, discouraging many investigators from using the *Journal of the American Chemical Society*. Those who were active in basic research, such as Charles Loring Jackson and Josiah Cooke of Harvard and Edward Williams Morley of Western Reserve University, had little regard for the journal and published very little in it.[16] Ira Remsen's attitude toward the periodical was probably representative. During one of his publications seminars at the Johns Hopkins, he spent considerable time pointing out the defects of the *Journal of the American Chemical Society* to his students. "And that," concluded Remsen, with evident disgust, slapping the publication down on the table, "that purports to be the official organ of American chemistry."[17]

Had the society's *Journal* been the only specialized organ available, American chemists would have used it more. The year of its establishment, however, witnessed the appearance of a far more successful periodical. Edited by Ira Remsen, the *American Chemical Journal* was a product of the graduate school movement in the United States. The immediate and heavy flow of research which came out of the Hopkins chemistry laboratory demanded an outlet. At first Remsen tried to place the material in Silliman's *Journal of Science:* but the "amount of material sent by me . . . frightened the editor [James Dwight Dana]," who returned the Hopkins articles with the suggestion that Remsen find some other place for them, "as they seemed too highly specialized and voluminous for a journal of general science."[18] Remsen's only course, as he saw it, was to establish his own publication.[19]

From the start the *American Chemical Journal* gave evidence that it intended to be a force for basic research. In the first issue appeared Wolcott Gibbs' article on the complex inorganic acids, Samuel Penfield's (Sheffield Scientific School) paper on a new method of determining fluorine, and Remsen's lengthy contribution

16. *General Index to the First Twenty Volumes, 1879-1898, Journal of the American Chemical Society* (Easton, Pennsylvania, 1902), 1-237.
17. Quoted in William A. Noyes and Jack F. Norris, "Ira Remsen," National Academy of Sciences, *Biographical Memoirs*, 14 (1932), 248.
18. Quoted in Frederick H. Getman, *The Life of Ira Remsen* (Easton, Pennsylvania, 1940), 49.
19. While deliberating the possibilities of setting up his own journal, Remsen placed the Hopkins research in the *Berichte der deutschen chemischen Gesellschaft*. See Noyes and Norris, 230-31.

on oxidation of substituted aromatic hydrocarbons.[20] Remsen's *Journal* emphasized basic research as no prior American periodical had done. Its book review and article abstracts sections seldom took note of material from the applied chemistry field. By opening the pages of his *Journal* to good graduate student research, Remsen helped establish publication as one of the imperatives of graduate work. In the 1890 volume, a representative one, student research contributions appeared from the laboratories of Harvard, Michigan, Clarke, Cornell, and Wesleyan universities.[21]

In the 1880's Remsen's *Journal* completely outclassed the *Journal of the American Chemical Society*. Changes were in prospect, however, which would radically reshape the latter publication. With the reorganization of the American Chemical Society, its journal finally became, as its founders intended it to be, a "clearing house for chemical news, research, and progress in America."[22] In 1893 society president Harvey Wiley took the first step toward rebuilding the publication by securing Edward Hart as its editor.

Hart, owner of a financially successful journal of applied chemistry, agreed to discontinue his publication and issue to his subscribers in its stead the near-defunct *Journal of the American Chemical Society*.[23] The *Journal* thus gained a ready-made base of support, but the job of rebuilding was a tough one. Hart found the publication six numbers behind schedule, with only two articles on hand. But with Wiley soliciting papers and Hart editing and printing them as fast as they came in, issues were soon appearing on schedule.[24]

20. Gibbs, "On the Complex Inorganic Acids," *American Chemical Journal*, 1 (1880), 109; S. L. Penfield, "On a New Volumetric Method of Determining Fluorine," *ibid.*, 27-29; Ira Remsen, "On the Oxidation of Substitution Products of Aromatic Hydrocarbons," *ibid.*, 52-66.

21. The Johns Hopkins University, *Register*, 1878-79:14; 1880-81:52; *American Chemical Journal*, 12 (1890), 1-594; Noyes and Norris, 231-34. According to Noyes and Norris' bibliography of Remsen's publications, the professor and his students (together) published thirty-one papers in the *American Chemical Journal* between the years 1879-1889.

22. Quoted in Charles A. Browne and Mary E. Weeks, *A History of the American Chemical Society* (Washington, 1952), 62.

23. Hart's journal was similar in content to the *American Chemist*, begun seventeen years earlier. The fact that *The Journal of Analytical and Applied Chemistry* prospered while the *American Chemist* did not was partially due to the fact that American industry, by the 1880's, was accepting the trained chemist as an important factor in its operations.

24. Browne and Weeks, 454, 497-98; Edward C. Bingham, "Edward Hart," *Journal of Industrial and Engineering Chemistry*, 5 (1923), 974-75.

The rapidly growing society was able to offer firm support to its *Journal*. In turn the publication offered a great deal to society members. By the 1890's the research contribution of American chemists had so increased that there was a real demand for another specialized journal. The increasing devotion of Remsen's magazine to the single field of organic chemistry heightened that need. Hart, meantime, as editor of the society's journal, opened his pages to both basic and applied investigations, in all branches of the science.[25]

In 1897 the American Chemical Society's publication began offering a service to American investigators that no prior periodical had attempted. That year editor Hart began providing a systematic and concise annual summary of all research that American workers had published during the year in any journal, chemical or nonchemical, American or foreign. Such a review was long overdue, for much American research continued to appear in nonprofessional or foreign organs and thus failed to become incorporated in the main body of literature. Hart's summary of chemical investigation not only enabled American professionals to stay abreast of research done by their colleagues, but it greatly enhanced the reputation of American chemical work abroad.[26]

By the mid-1890's American chemists had at their disposal two journals of national and international scope in which to record the results of their work. The next ten years were to add the final chapter in the development of a system of American chemical publications. Owing to the rapid growth of specialized branches of chemistry, American workers in the science began to feel the need for more highly specialized journals, and during this period they took steps to establish them. In 1896 two Cornell University professors, Wilder Bancroft and Joseph Trevor, established the *Journal of Physical Chemistry*. Six years later a group of university and industrial chemists founded the American Electro-chemical Society whose *Proceedings* provided a place for research in this branch. In 1906 J. J. Abel of the Johns Hopkins and C. A. Herter of New York, two physiological chemists, began the publication of the *Journal of Biological Chemistry*. These journals freed American

25. Browne and Weeks, 508; see "Index," *American Chemical Journal,* 7 (1886), iii-iv; 12 (1890), iii-vii; *General Index to the First Twenty Volumes, 1879-98, Journal of the American Chemical Society,* 1-237.
26. Browne and Weeks, 69.

chemists from a dependence on European, particularly German, periodicals in the newer branches of chemistry. The founding of these specialized American journals signified the attainment of American self-sufficiency in chemical publication. And with their establishment the American chemical profession severed the last bond of dependency which tied it to Europe.[27]

27. *The Journal of Physical Chemistry*, 1 (1897), title page; *Proceedings of the American Electro-chemical Society*, 1 (1902), title page; *The Journal of Biological Chemistry*, 1 (1906), title page. Otto Folin, Harvard biochemist, was characteristic of turn-of-the-century American chemists who no longer had to rely on German journals after the establishment of the specialized American publications. Up to the early 1900's Folin's research appeared largely in the German *Zeitschrift für physiologische Chemie*, but beginning in 1907 Folin prepared most of his work for publication in the new *Journal of Biological Chemistry*. See P. A. Shaffer, "Otto Folin," National Academy of Sciences, *Biographical Memoirs*, 27 (1952), 72-74.

5. THE CHEMIST AT WORK

TEACHING

The number of chemists in college, scientific school, and university teaching positions in the last half of the nineteenth century far exceeded the combined total in the other major employing agencies, government and industry.[1] Although the number of chemists in America rose rapidly, from 465 in 1850 to nearly 9,000 in 1900, teaching positions in insitutions of higher education expanded to keep pace.[2] While the individual chemist entering upon a teaching career through this fifty-year period probably did not enjoy any relative improvement in the number of posts open to him, this period did bring significant changes in the demands made upon him by educational institutions. His role within the institutions also changed.

In the 1850's and 1860's the chemistry professor in the liberal arts college seldom had specialized academic training for his work. His usual credentials were a classical college diploma or a degree from a medical school. The duties of the college chemist ordinarily extended to two or more disciplines, and his work consisted largely of conducting lectures and recitations. Facilities for experimentation were almost nonexistent. If the professor of chemistry had his own laboratory he probably had to furnish it at his own expense; seldom were faculty members as fortunate as Silas Douglass, professor of chemistry, mineralogy, and geology at the University of Michigan, who tapped the largess of that institution for $50 to equip a private laboratory.[3]

The experience of Ezra Carr at the University of Wisconsin was broadly representative of those of other chemistry professors of the 1850's and 1860's. Carr was a graduate of Rensselaer Polytechnic Institute and the Castleton, Vermont, Medical College. In

1. A survey of chemists appearing in the *National Cyclopaedia of American Biography* who entered upon their professional careers in the nineteenth century showed that 140 of 180 chemists made teaching their life's work.

2. Department of Commerce and Labor, Bureau of the Census, *Occupations at the Twelfth Census* (Washington, 1904), xxxiv-xxxv.

3. Burke A. Hinsdale, *History of the University of Michigan* (Ann Arbor, 1906), 113; Douglass, November 7, 1881, to Henry F. Frieze, Henry F. Frieze Papers, Michigan Historical Collections of the University of Michigan.

1856 he joined the Wisconsin faculty. In appointing him to the chair of chemistry and natural history the Wisconsin regents stated that it would be Carr's duty to "render courses of instruction in Chemistry and its applications, mineralogy, geology, the Natural History of Plants and Animals and Human Physiology." Carr also had the duty of maintaining the collections in the physical sciences, and he was required "to make and publish meteorological observations."[4] After a year of service Carr complained to the regents that the teaching of science required peculiar means and methods, and that if the university did not supply such means he could not develop his subjects properly. To force the teaching of the sciences to conform to the methods of other departments, Carr said, "would be like requiring the Engineers to use the tools of the watchmaker."[5]

Although such conditions prevailed generally in the 1850's and 1860's, improvements were in prospect through the scientific school movement. The scientific schools and departments chose specialists to man their faculties in each branch of science. The selection of the specialist over the medical doctor or the graduate from a classical college marked the beginning of a standard of preparation for chemists in institutions of higher education. The scientific school professor was usually no less burdened with teaching duties than his brother in the classical college but, unlike the college chemist, he did have the opportunity to work solely in his own field. Furthermore, the scientific schools recognized the importance of laboratory instruction and provided facilities for experimentation, which the professor could use for his own work if he could find time.

The second development of the 1850's and 1860's which affected the position of the academic chemist was the movement for federal support of technical education, which culminated in the passage of the Morrill Act. Between 1862 and the end of the century 56 new institutions came into being as a result of the land-grant act. Nearly all of them demanded the services of the professor of chemistry.[6] The quality of institutions created by the act was by

4. Carr, November 21, 1849, report to Regents, p. 13, *Regents Records*, University of Wisconsin Library.

5. July 25, 1857, report to Regents, p. 141, Record Book "B," *Regents Records*.

6. United States Bureau of Education, *Report of the Commissioner of Education*, 2 (Washington, 1901), 1813-26.

no means uniform: many of the new institutions offered the college chemist little opportunity to improve his position. The Florida State College of Agriculture revealed its conception of science by establishing a professorship of agriculture, horticulture, and Greek.[7] Most land-grant institutions were unable to provide their early faculties with adequate facilities and equipment because of their precarious financial position. Federal funds proved inadequate to meet the costs of technical education and, until the late 1880's, state governments for the most part were unwilling to give supplemental support.[8] But the Morrill Act did permit the establishment of strong chemistry departments in many instances, and such departments offered inviting opportunities to American chemists. In 1867 the newly organized Illinois Industrial University (later the University of Illinois) used the state's grant to set up a program which embraced full courses of analytical and practical chemistry. The university proceeded immediately to build a laboratory and hired a professor whose sole duties were in the field of chemistry.[9]

In the 1870's and 1880's, despite the improvements in professional position worked by the scientific school movement and the land-grant act, most college chemists labored under a heavy teaching burden, found little opportunity to specialize, and had to make the most of inadequate facilities. At the University of Michigan, one of the "better" institutions so far as science was concerned, chemist John W. Langley reported that his instructional and other duties made heavy demands on him. He complained that all of his time "except that necessary for eating and studying and a portion of the evenings was virtually given to university work."[10]

In the smaller colleges the professor of chemistry was in an even worse position. In 1884 Lombard College (Illinois) sought a man to teach "Chemistry, Physiology, Botany, Zoology, German, etc." and specified that it wanted a "first rate man."[11] A young instructor in analytical chemistry at Cornell, F. W. Rich, took the job, though

7. Richard Hofstadter and Dewitt Hardy, *The Development & Scope of Higher Education in the United States* (New York, 1952), 40-41.

8. E. D. Ross, *Democracy's College* (Ames, Iowa, 1942), 98.

9. Illinois Industrial University, *Report of the Committee on Courses of Study & Faculty (1867)*, 5; IIU, *Annual Register*, 1870-71, 33.

10. John W. Langley Papers, 1875-76, Michigan Historical Collections of the University of Michigan.

11. J. N. Standish, July 22, 1884, to Stephen M. Babcock, Box 2 of Correspondence, Stephen M. Babcock Papers, Wisconsin Historical Society Library, Madison.

skeptical about its possibilities. "If they include Greek, Sanskrit, and Christian Ethics," said Rich, "I am afraid my qualifications will not fill the bill."[12] Soon Rich was thoroughly disgusted with the position. Laboratory apparatus was almost nonexistent, and he found it impossible to extract even $50 from the college for equipment and chemicals.[13]

While F. W. Rich's troubles at Lombard College were characteristic of those of most teaching chemists in the 1870's and 1880's, conditions were steadily improving. There was a growing recognition in leading institutions of the need for academic specialization. In 1876 University of Wisconsin President John Bascom stated that superior instruction was not possible without a subdivision of labor. Evidence that Bascom was able to translate this view into action was the relief given to Professor W. W. Daniells, whose experience illustrated what was happening on other campuses. In 1868 Daniells began his Wisconsin career, responsible for instruction in agriculture and analytical chemistry, but in 1879 the university relieved him of all but his chemistry duties.[14]

The academic chemist continued to bring more specialized training to his teaching duties. By the late 1860's the M.D. and the man with the classical education began to hold fewer chemistry positions. In this same decade, men trained at American scientific schools or in the German universities began to have first claim on the most sought-for teaching posts.[15] Faculty appointments at Cornell University in the period from the late 1860's to the 1880's, revealed the demand for the chemist with specialized training. When Cornell began instruction in 1868 its first two appointments in chemistry went to George Caldwell, Ph.D. from Göttingen University, and James M. Crafts, a Lawrence Scientific School graduate and student of several European universities. In 1869 Charles S. Shaeffer, a Göttingen Ph.D., received the third

12. August 6, 1884 to Babcock, Box 3, Babcock Papers.
13. October 18, 1884, to Babcock, Box 3, Babcock Papers.
14. Merle Curti and Vernon Carstensen, *The University of Wisconsin, 1848-1925* (2 volumes, Madison, 1945), 1:331; The University of Wisconsin *General Catalogue,* 1849-83:11.
15. The *National Cyclopaedia* survey showed Albert Prescott to be the last chemist trained as an M.D. to hold a college chemical position. Prescott received an appointment in chemistry at the University of Michigan in 1864. The last classical college graduate (with no further schooling in chemistry) to hold a college teaching position was J. B. Herreshoff, who obtained an appointment in chemistry at Brown in 1869.

Cornell appointment, and the next year Chester Wing, Lawrence Scientific School student, got the fourth.[16]

The 1870's and 1880's brought an increasing recognition from college and university trustees that chemistry professors could not operate effectively within the confines of the lecture-textbook-recitation system of instruction. By the 1870's the laboratory method, applied so successfully in a handful of colleges and scientific schools earlier in the century, was used with increasing frequency. By 1880 roughly one-half of the 343 colleges, universities, and scientific schools in the United States maintained laboratories of some description for instruction in chemistry.[17]

Before the 1870's heavy teaching loads (even when all instruction fell into one discipline), with such other added tasks as monitoring student behavior, prevented American professors in all fields of learning from doing much research. Men like Wolcott Gibbs and Josiah Cooke did make important contributions to chemical knowledge, but they were merely the exceptions which proved the rule. What those men did, they did largely on their own time during hours stolen from the small measure of leisure which remained after a heavy work day. In the third quarter of the nineteenth century no institution made it a matter of policy to aid the research efforts of its faculty.

With the establishment of the Johns Hopkins University, however, America got such an institution. From the outset Hopkins pledged to keep its professors "free from petty cares, and to encourage them to advance, by researchers and publications, the sciences they profess."[18] The existence of the Johns Hopkins forced each institution of higher education to recognize the research function of the professor. And every university in existence in 1876, or

16. W. T. Hewett, *Cornell University: A History* (4 volumes, New York, 1905), 2:162, 165.

17. F. W. Clarke, *A Report on the Teaching of Chemistry and Physics in the U.S. Circular of the Bureau of Education, 1880* (Washington, 1881), 167-68, Table II. The quality of laboratories in the United States varied widely. Some offered only qualitative analysis work (an operation requiring the very minimum in equipment); from this level the quality of laboratories ranged all the way up to those which had the equipment for instruction in all the branches of chemistry, plus facilities for research. But the quality of the laboratory was not the important thing. What was important was that the existence of some kind of laboratory represented a concession by the institution that chemistry had certain unique needs that had to be met in nontraditional ways.

18. Johns Hopkins Register 1880-81, 21.

founded thereafter, had to decide whether to adopt the Hopkins model or settle for a lesser aim.

The last decade of the century saw a steady improvement in the academic chemist's position. The laboratory method of instruction was by this time standard practice. In 1901 the American Chemical Society, surveying the teaching of chemistry, concluded that no American institution of higher education attempted instruction without laboratory equipment. Minimum standards for the teaching of chemistry continued to rise. For positions in the better endowed private institutions and the larger state universities, graduate training was essential, and the Ph.D. was fast becoming the standard of acceptability.[19]

Heavy teaching loads in the nineties were the lot of most academic chemists. According to one spokesman, all American chemistry teachers had "a common complaint to voice. They will tell you the demands made upon them as instructors are alone culpable for their meager contributions to . . . research. Too many hours of teaching. Too many subjects to be taught."[20] Improvements were in the offing, however. In the 1890's the better endowed universities began to use young, low-paid instructors and assistants to ease the load on their full professors.[21] Harvard was an example. In 1895 Chemistry Professor Charles Loring Jackson gave only two courses. A force of eleven assistants and instructors carried the load in the elementary courses, providing the senior faculty with the time to conduct their own research.[22]

By the 1890's the research idea had taken a firm hold, at least at the larger institutions. Even the overworked assistant professors and instructors, feeling that the employing institution and the chemistry profession in general expected some research effort from

19. American Chemical Society, *Twenty-fifth Anniversary of the American Chemical Society* (Easton, Pennsylvania, 1902), 101. Regarding the emergence of the Ph.D. in chemistry teaching, the *National Cyclopaedia* survey showed that of 28 chemists who entered teaching in the nineties (or shortly after), 26 had advanced training in chemistry. Of these 26, 22 had Ph.D's—15 from United States universities. These 28 chemists, by and large, joined the faculties of wealthy private or large state institutions.

20. W. E. Stone, "The Relation of Teaching to Research," *Journal of the American Chemical Society*, 15 (1893), 666.

21. A. G. Mayer, "Material vs. the Intellectual Development of our Universities," *Science*, 20 (1904), 45; Kuno Francke, "A Difference in German and American University Methods," *The Nation*, 50 (1890), 132-33.

22. T. W. Richards, "The Chemistry Laboratory," *Harvard Graduates Magazine*, 4 (1895-96), 248-49.

them, made such contributions as they could. In 1897 Assistant Professor T. W. Richards of Harvard published a paper on the atomic weight of magnesium and strontium.[23] At about the same time at the University of Michigan, Chemistry Instructor David M. Lichty was able to report that he had "carried on a little investigation in chemistry."[24]

Specialization proceeded apace in the 1890's. Owing to the rapid increase in the body of chemical knowledge, particularly in the new branches of physical and physiological chemistry, American colleges and universities were forced to concede the impossibility of one man's teaching all the branches. Accordingly, in the last decade of the century educational institutions began to parcel out small segments of the field to individual professors. In 1889 the University of Wisconsin made former instructor H. W. Hillyer an assistant professor of organic chemistry. In 1893 Louis Kahlenberg joined the Wisconsin faculty as instructor in chemistry; three years later the university narrowed his title to instructor in physical chemistry.[25]

STATE AND MUNICIPAL GOVERNMENT WORK

Prior to 1870 geological surveys undertaken by the several states provided the principal nonacademic jobs for American chemists. Other state agencies such as the gas commissions (to oversee the manufacture of illuminating gas from coal), agricultural boards, and assaying offices also used their services. The places for chemists on the surveys, however, exceeded the total of all other state openings.[26]

The period from 1830 until the outbreak of the Civil War was a time of great activity in state surveying. Those decades saw surveys undertaken by such states as Pennsylvania, New York, New Hampshire, Alabama, Illinois, Wisconsin, California, and Missouri. State survey work did not offer very stable employment, for once the field study was completed and the findings published, the survey died. Most chemists in fact looked upon this work as a way

23. *Harvard Graduates Magazine*, 5 (1896-97), 237-39.

24. October 4, 1899, to "Members of the Nine," Michigan Historical Collection of the University of Michigan.

25. Wisconsin Catalogues, 1849-87:16, 18; 1849-97:28; *National Cyclopaedia*, 15:138; 16:424; 25:73.

26. The *National Cyclopaedia* survey of chemists showed that up to 1870, 17 chemists found survey work and only 7 engaged in all other state supported activity (of the 7, some held survey jobs also—I counted such chemists twice).

to get experience until a more permanent position appeared. Irish-born John W. Mallet, a German university graduate, used the survey in that manner. Mallet came to the United States in 1853. His first job was chemist to the Alabama Survey; he retained this connection only until 1856 when he received an appointment to the chair of chemistry at the University of Alabama.[27]

The state surveys called upon the chemist for many skills. He worked as mineralogist, metallurgist, and geologist, in addition to performing strictly chemical services. The fact that the chemist was prepared to render other services and the fact that the survey expected them from him reflected the lack of specialization in the sciences in the middle decades of the nineteenth century. The surveys did, however, set a precedent by turning from the beginning to the chemist with formal training in the sciences instead of to the M.D. or the graduate of the classical college.

With the exception of California and a few other states, the Civil War brought a temporary suspension to survey work. After the war survey activity began once more. The surveys undertaken in the decades following the war, however, differed from those of the prewar period in that an increasing number were organized on a permanent basis; by the turn of the century most states had continuing surveys. Although most of those agencies employed chemists only part time, about one-third of the permanent surveys hired them as regular staff members. The Wisconsin survey fell into the latter category: a chemist worked full time in its division of soils. In the state surveys of the postwar period the chemist found fewer openings, but when he obtained a place as a regular staff member, he enjoyed a permanence of position not found before.[28]

In the post-Civil War period geological surveys were no longer the only state agencies which made a large call upon the chemist's services. The 1860's and 1870's were the inaugural years of the municipal and state boards of health and the state agricultural

27. *National Cyclopaedia*, 1:348; 6:191; 9:120; 13:55; 11:91; 9:214; 10:503.

28. M. M. Leighton, compiler, *Summary Information on the State Geological Surveys and the United States Geological Survey* (Bulletin 188 of the National Research Council, Washington, 1932), 1-136; C. W. Hayes, compiler, *The State Geological Surveys of the United States* (United States Geological Survey Bulletin, 465, Washington, 1911), 1-777. On the matter of opportunity for chemists in the surveys of the period 1865-1900, the *National Cyclopedia* survey of chemists showed fourteen chemists employed by state surveys prior to 1870 and only five employed in the years after 1870.

experiment stations. Chemistry, because it was able to show its applicability to matters of health and agriculture, quickly found a place in these new agencies.

One of the factors accounting for the advent of the public health movement was the rise of the American city. Crowded and squalid living conditions which accompanied urbanization promoted the spread of infectious disease. The concentration of large numbers of people in big cities, where they were subject to the ravages of disease, forced Americans to deal with problems of public health. The epidemics that swept the cities of the United States taught the lesson that not even the comfortable classes were safe from cholera and yellow fever.

Scientific advance was a second factor that explained the public health movement. While it did not yet have the answers to the question of disease mechanism (Robert Koch, famous German bacteriologist, did not discover the cholera bacteria until 1883), science was able to show that such simple precautions as the boiling of water and the disinfecting of clothes and bedding would drastically curtail the spread of epidemics.[29] When cholera hit the nation in 1866, public opinion and science were both ready to meet the challenge. The first permanent public health boards arose as a response to that epidemic.

From the late 1860's through the 1880's, 32 states established boards of health. Louisiana was first (1867), followed by Massachusetts (1869), and California (1870). Michigan established its board in 1873, Illinois in 1877, and New York in 1880. Municipalities also set up health agencies. New York City, with its Metropolitan Board of Health (1866), led the nation in the movement.[30]

In determining the function of these boards, city and state administrators recognized that such tasks as water and soil analysis, inspection of milk, and control of manufacture and sale of kerosene were essential to the public health. They recognized, further, that the chemist was best equipped to perform these tasks, and so gave him a position on the health boards.

Charles F. Chandler, Göttingen University graduate and Columbia University professor, was connected with the Metropolitan

29. Charles Rosenberg, *The Cholera Years* (Chicago, 1961), especially pp. 193-200 on the effects of these precautionary measures in New York City.
30. *Ibid.*, 192-93; N. S. Shaler, *The United States of America* (2 volumes, New York, 1894), 2:557-58.

Board of Health (New York City) from its beginning. His experience was representative of that of other chemists in public health service. Chandler's employment also illustrated the continuance of the tradition established by the state surveys of the specialist in public work. For 16 years Professor Chandler served the New York City board on a part-time basis. During this period he investigated such problems as city water and milk supplies, adulterated liquors, poisonous cosmetics, improper plumbing and drainage in tenements, and kerosene explosions.

Chandler's work in connection with the kerosene problem illustrated the specific function of the chemist on the health board. In the 1860's kerosene was beginning to replace coal oil as an illuminating fluid. In its pure form kerosene was safe, but blended with more volatile fluids it could be highly explosive. Many of the New York City grocers found that they could boost their profits by mixing kerosene with benzene or naphtha, cheaper but highly volatile substances. The result of this mixing was an explosion a day in the city.

Chandler sought to arouse city officials to the menace of blended kerosene. In an 1870 article he reported that five people, four of them children, died in a single month in Brooklyn owing to kerosene explosions. No adjective was strong enough, said Chandler, to "stigmatize the crime of selling benzene . . . as a specially safe article, to spread death and destruction among helpless women and children. . . . We shudder," he said, "at the thought of a man who was murdered for a pair of boots, but these . . . persons were murdered for a difference of five cents a gallon in the cost of dangerous and unsafe kerosene."[31] To back up his claims about the danger of blending, Chandler collected samples of adulterated kerosene and in the board's chemistry laboratory he carried out chemical tests on both pure and mixed samples. His published results proved both the danger of the blended product and the safety of the pure article. Chandler's experiments, along with his crusading articles, led eventually to the adoption of a city code to regulate kerosene sale.[32]

The first agricultural experiment stations appeared about a decade after the start of the public health movement, offering chemists

31. "Dangerous Kerosene," *The American Chemist*, 1 (1871), 123.
32. *Ibid.*, 13:57; M. T. Bogert, "C. F. Chandler," National Academy of Sciences, *Biographical Memoirs*, 14 (1932), 161-63.

additional employment opportunities. The application of science, particularly chemistry, to the promotion of American agriculture was an old theme. In 1832 Benjamin Silliman, Sr., wrote a manual dealing with the cultivation and refining of sugar cane. In the 1840's and 1850's Liebig's laboratory was the mecca for American students interested in agricultural chemistry. In 1862 the creation of a Department of Agriculture and the passage of the Morrill Act gave further impetus to the movement toward scientific agriculture.[33]

Founded to provide indoor and outdoor research laboratories to supplement instruction in agricultural science in the land-grant colleges, the first experiment station appeared in Connecticut in 1875. Other states soon followed Connecticut's lead. By 1880 North Carolina had its experiment station. New York organized its station in 1881, and Massachusetts followed a year later. In 1887 the federal government spurred the movement with the passage of the Hatch Act, which provided continuing funds for the operation of a station in every state.[34] The experiment station movement opened up many positions for chemists, providing places for 150 of them by the end of the century.[35]

Chemists considered the agricultural experiment station positions "choice" jobs, both in respect to salary and function. Charles Dabney, Göttingen Ph.D. and director of the North Carolina station, was well pleased with his position. He had considered a teaching post at the University of North Carolina but took the station directorship because "the University . . . is poor, while the state is very liberal to this enterprise."[36] Station chemists had to perform much work of a routine technical nature, analyzing fertilizers and plants, marls, mineral waters, and various agricultural products, and they had a heavy load of administrative work. Dabney com-

33. C. A. Browne, "History of Chemical Education in America, 1820-1870," *Journal of Chemical Education*, 9 (1932), 718-20.

34. In the establishment of the Connecticut, Massachusetts, North Carolina, and New York stations, see R. H. Chittenden, "W. H. Brewer," National Academy, *Memoirs*, 12 (1929), 307; Massachusetts Agricultural College, *Charles A. Goessmann* (Cambridge, 1917), 114; C. W. Dabney, December 13, 1880, to Babcock, Box 2, Babcock Papers; *First Annual Report of the Board of Control of the New York State Agricultural Experiment Station for the Year, 1882* (Albany, 1883), 2-3; on the purpose of experiment stations, see A. Hunter Dupree, *Science in the Federal Government* (Cambridge, 1957), 170.

35. American Chemical Society, *Twenty-fifth Anniversary*, 158.

36. December 13, 1880, to Babcock, Box 2, Babcock Papers.

plained that correspondence with the farmers of North Carolina was "very burdensome."[37]

In spite of their routine functions, the experiment stations slowly developed into centers of agricultural chemical research. This was possible because they were on a fairly sound financial footing—especially after the passage of the Hatch Act—and could afford both the equipment for investigations and the personnel to take the load of routine work off the shoulders of the investigator. In December, 1880, Dabney reported joyfully that he was "entitled to *four* assistants," with a fifth to come "the 1st of Jan."[38] The personal factor counted heavily in the research orientation of the stations. The chemists who manned those posts were generally men who knew how to use the relative freedom of the station position. Trained in the graduate schools of America or Germany, those investigators brought a high regard for scientific research to their agricultural work.

Göttingen-trained Ph.D. Stephen M. Babcock was one professional who accepted an experiment station position just as the movement was gathering momentum. Over the course of his career he enjoyed increasing opportunities to pursue his own research interests. His experience in that regard was broadly representative of those workers in other stations and reflected the evolution of the experiment stations as laboratories of agricultural research.

In 1882, after several industrial and academic opportunities misfired, Babcock accepted a position as chemist to the newly established New York (Geneva) Experiment Station.[39] In the initial years his work consisted largely of making routine chemical analyses of vegetables and milk. By 1885, however, an assistant performed most of those tasks and Babcock was able to concentrate on his special interest, the chemistry of milk and milk products. In 1886 he investigated the viscosity (resistance of liquids to flow) of milk in an effort to determine the factors affecting it. That interest led to the invention of a viscosity measuring device, and it

37. *Ibid.;* on the matter of routine technical work, see H. W. Wiley, June 4, 1887, E. H. Jenkins, September 2, 1887, and Dudley Miller, June 1, 1887, to Babcock, Box 3, Babcock Papers.
38. December 13, 1880, letter to Babcock, Box 2, Babcock Papers.
39. E. L. Sturtevant, April 14, 1882, James Y. McKee, May 5, 1882, E. L. Sturtevant, May 19, 1882, to Babcock, Box 2, Babcock Papers. See Babcock, May 10, 1882, to J. Y. McKee, Box 2, Babcock Papers.

was not long before Babcock's abilities were attracting the notice of agricultural scientists throughout the country.[40]

In 1887 W. A. Henry, dean of the University of Wisconsin College of Agriculture, decided that his experiment station and college needed a good dairy scientist like Babcock. Satisfied with his Geneva post, the New York chemist resisted Dean Henry's initial overtures, despite the latter's promise of a light teaching schedule and ample time for research.[41] But Henry persevered, assuring Babcock that there were "no discords nor dissentions" at Wisconsin and that his "ambition here would cross no other man's path."[42] By the end of 1887 Babcock was convinced and accepted the Wisconsin offer.[43]

In large measure the Wisconsin station allowed Babcock to roam freely over whatever scientific terrain he chose. Dairymen the world over benefited from that policy. With Station Bacteriologist H. L. Russell, Babcock solved the mystery of cheese-ripening and gave dairymen the important cold-cure process of making cheese. His butterfat test for milk was another important contribution. Not only did it work a revolution in agricultural marketing, but it made the name Babcock a household word to the American farmer.[44]

FEDERAL GOVERNMENT WORK

From 1850 to the end of the century the prospects of the chemist in federal government service passed through three distinct phases. Until the 1860's the chemist found almost no place for his services in the established agencies of the federal government. The few exceptions only proved the rule. In 1855 Eugene W. Hillgard, recently returned to the United States with his Ph.D. from Heidelberg University, served three years as director of the Smithsonian chemistry laboratory. But in this period the laboratory needed only one chemist. A few chemists worked on agricultural

40. Babcock, in the *Annual Report of the New York Experiment Station,* 1885:267, 1886:297-310; H. W. Wiley, July 4, 1887, Dudley Miller, June 1, 1887, to Babcock, Box 3, Babcock Papers.

41. Henry, August 31, 1887, to Babcock, Box 3, Babcock Papers.

42. September 16, 1887, to Babcock, Box 3, Babcock Papers.

43. T. C. Chamerlin, October 26, 1887, to Babcock, Box 3, Babcock Papers.

44. H. L. Russell, "Man of Science," *Stephen M. Babcock,* 5-6 (Publication of Wisconsin Alumni Research Foundation). Babcock, December 28, 1895, January 26, 1896, January 31, 1896, and March 22, 1896, to May Crandall, Box 3, Babcock Papers. Wisconsin Catalogue, 1899-1900:3, 229-34.

problems for the Patent Office (the home of government agricultural activities before 1862), but only on a part-time, contract basis.[45]

The main opportunity for federal employment was, as in the state governments, in geological surveys. Those undertaken prior to the Civil War, with the exception of the Coast and Geodetic Survey which made few calls upon the chemist, usually had short-term assignments. Chemists connected with them enjoyed only brief employment.[46]

In the 1860's the second phase of government scientific activity began. For the next twenty years the government was involved in the work of enlarging its scientific structure, while at the same time wrestling with the problem of its proper organization. In 1862 Congress created the Department of Agriculture. Chemistry found a home in the new department, but the off-and-on character of federal sponsorship rendered the chemist's position uncertain. Reflecting this uncertainty was the fact that between 1862 and 1883 the post of chief chemist to the department changed hands on the average of every four years.[47]

Charles M. Wetherill was the first professional chemist to serve in the new Department of Agriculture. His experience reflected the trials of chemists in that department. When Wetherill began his work in the department in 1862 his salary came out of the department's general fund, since Congress had made no specific appropriation to cover it. During Wetherill's tenure of office the department had no laboratory of its own, so that he had to do all of his work in the Patent Office's dark and damp basement laboratory. His agricultural work was chiefly concerned with studies of sugar production, but since he was the only chemist then in the federal service, the government used him for many purposes entirely unconnected with agriculture.

One of these nonagricultural assignments led eventually to Wetherill's dismissal. In 1863 President Lincoln pulled him away from his agricultural duties to investigate a new gunpowder for the government. All agricultural work ground to a halt. Lincoln in fact gave instructions for Wetherill to "close his laboratory in the

45. *National Cyclopaedia*, 10:308; G. A. Weber, *The Bureau of Chemistry and Soils* (Baltimore, 1928), 8.
46. *National Cyclopaedia*, 12:260; 11:337.
47. Weber, 15, 18; see pp. 1-40.

Agriculture Department . . . and to take his key with him for the security of its contents."[48] Commissioner of Agriculture Isaac Newton, a former dairy farmer with political ambitions, took a dim view of Lincoln's removing his only chemist. When Wetherill returned, Newton denied him his back pay, claiming that his absence had disrupted the entire department. Lincoln urged Newton to yield on the salary matter, but Newton, in a display of independence, not only ignored Lincoln but fired Wetherill permanently. Not even a special Congressional inquiry could restore Wetherill to his post.[49]

The period from the 1860's to the 1880's also witnessed an increase in the geological survey activity of the federal government. From 1867 to 1873 four large surveys with a semipermanent tenure entered the field, replacing the earlier, scattered efforts. In developing more permanent surveys, federal activity coincided with that of the states. In the federal surveys of the 1860's and 1870's, however, there was no formal place for chemistry, as there was in the Department of Agriculture, and places for chemists were no greater in number than had existed in earlier federal surveys.[50] But as a transition stage between the scattered surveys of the 1850's and 1860's and the tightly organized and permanent United States Geological Survey, which came later, these intermediate surveys were important to the advance of chemistry in the federal service.

The 1880's marked the beginning of the third phase of the chemist's connection with the federal government. That decade produced a more stable organization of science. The chemist profited by this new stability, and in such developments as the permanent recognition of a chemical division within the Department of Agriculture and the creation of a chemical section in the United States Geological Survey, the chemist found permanence of position and an increasing appreciation of his services.

48. April 4, 1863, to Isaac Newton, quoted in Smith, "Charles Meyer Wetherill," *Journal of Chemical Education*, 6 (1929), 1673; see also 1828-73.
49. Smith, 1675-80; Dupree, 152.
50. Dupree, 195-202, 384. The *National Cyclopaedia* survey showed one chemist on the four surveys that functioned between 1867 and 1879. There had been 14 who served on the earlier (pre-1867) ones. Evidently these surveys in the intermediate period of government scientific activity offered no more places to chemists than the earlier ones had done—and they probably offered fewer places.

In 1881 the government regularized the support of the chemistry division of the Department of Agriculture. Two years later the division got its first permanent director: Harvey W. Wiley. Under Wiley's leadership the range of operations of the chemistry division expanded measurably. Wiley determined not only to continue the sugar studies carried on in previous years, "but to enlarge them and place them on a more practical foundation."[51]

The work that led to great expansion in the size of the chemistry division, however, was its study of food and drugs. Soon after taking office Wiley launched his campaign against harmful food additives. Combining careful chemical experimentation with sensationalism (the "Poison Squad"), Wiley and the men of his division sought to awaken the public to the dangers inherent in the unregulated manufacture of food. Drugs also came under the scrutiny of the division, which warned the public against harmful quack medicines, habit-forming headache remedies, and opium cough syrups with which unsuspecting mothers "doped their babies into insensibility at night."[52]

Through his food and drug work Wiley aimed not only to safeguard the public health but also to gain public support for remedial legislation. In the Pure Food and Drug Act of 1906, Wiley's efforts finally met with success.[53] This law, by giving regulatory power to the Chemistry Bureau (the division had become a bureau in 1901), brought about a tremendous increase in the size of the chemical agency of the Agriculture Department. In 1906 just before the law was passed, Wiley's chemical staff numbered 110; by 1908 it had expanded to 425.[54]

After 1880 the chemist also found increased opportunity for employment in the federal survey. In 1879 Congress consolidated the four western surveys into one agency, the United States Geological Survey. This was an important development, since the vast scope of the new survey demanded a more formal organization of its chemical work. In 1880 Clarence King, the first director, recognized this and set up the survey's first chemical laboratory at Denver, Colorado. The second director, John Wesley Powell, added two more laboratories and in 1890 centralized all the chemical work in one laboratory in Washington, D. C.[55]

51. Wiley, *Autobiography* (Indianapolis, 1930), 168.
52. *Ibid.*, 207; also see 198-209.   53. *Ibid.*, 215-21.
54. Dupree, 179, 385; Weber, 18; Wiley, 233.

The primary work of this laboratory was to assist geologists in the identification of their collections. Standard analyses of such materials as minerals, coals, ores, and waters occupied a large part of the survey chemist's time. Routine work was not the sole fare, however. The analyses themselves often demanded that the chemist contrive new investigative procedures. Furthermore, the Geological Survey was more than willing to have its chemists engage in abstract research. According to the chief chemist, F. W. Clarke, work of his division was "not limited by utilitarian considerations," but was "also distinctly scientific in its aims." The attitude in the survey was that "the geologist could be aided fully as much by chemical researches as by mere routine analysis."[56]

The work of chemist W. F. Hillebrand illustrated the freedom granted to survey workers. In the course of his career in Washington he built a reputation as a leading analytical chemist. The techniques he devised were famous for their sensitivity. In 1887 he came close to achieving the ultimate in his specialty— the discovery of an element. While analyzing uranitite he found, to his surprise, that nitrogen evolved from the mineral. Hillebrand suspected that some other element might be contained in the nitrogen, but he did not pursue this suspicion and published his investigation as it stood. William Ramsay, English chemist and discoverer of the ideal gas, argon, noted the American's findings and undertook an investigation on cleveite, a first cousin to Hillebrand's mineral. Ramsay found no nitrogen in cleveite, but he did find helium, an element previously thought to exist only on the sun. Later, investigating Hillebrand's mineral, Ramsay found that the "other element" suspected by the American was also helium.[57]

While the chemical sections of the Department of Agriculture and the Geological Survey were the main centers of activity in the federal government from the 1880's to the turn of the century, they were by no means the only places open to chemists. With the expansion of the scientific function of the government, chemists found niches in many agencies. Prior to 1900 the Bureau of Animal Industry, the Dairy Division, and the Division of Vegetable Physiology and Pathology (all in the Department of Agriculture) em-

55. F. W. Clarke, "The Chemical Work of the United States Geological Survey," *Science*, 30 (1909), 161, 170.

56. *Ibid.*, 170; also see 161, 165-66.   57. Ibid., 54-55; *DAB*, 9:50-51.

ployed chemists. Some very unlikely agencies also required chemical services: in 1887 chemist Edgar Richards joined the United States Treasury Department, to aid in the regulation of oleomargarine sales.[58]

INDUSTRIAL WORK

Relative to the number of operational units American industry made far less call upon the services of the chemist throughout the nineteenth century than did educational institutions or the agencies of government.[59] Up to about the 1870's the chemist had almost no place in the American industrial order. The purely chemical industry was almost nonexistent, and to the extent that chemical establishments did exist, rule of thumb methods largely governed their operations. A few chemists found work with drug firms, coal oil and petroleum distilleries, gas works, cottonseed oil plants, and metal smelting works. But a chemist to many of these firms was very often a person who had had very little formal schooling and who was self-taught in his trade. Luther Atwood was an example of the chemical tinker in industry. As a boy Atwood learned the art of distilling on his farm, where he set up a small contrivance to manufacture peppermint oil. This experience brought a demand for his services from several firms in the coal oil and petroleum distilling business. From 1848 until his death Atwood found steady employment with such firms as the Philbrick and Trafton Chemical Company of Boston and the American Kerosene Gas Light Company of New Jersey, and for one period in the mid-1850's Atwood successfully operated his own distillation firm.[60]

Between 1840 and 1870 the chemist had as much chance to secure a place in industry by starting his own business as he did by attempting to locate a position with an established firm.[61] In the

58. *National Cyclopaedia*, 11:54; 10:238; 26:86.

59. The *National Cyclopaedia* survey showed that in the years from 1870 to the turn of the century, industry employed 31 survey chemists while educational institutions hired about 70; health and agricultural agencies—city and state—employed 26; and the federal government had places for 13.

60. Frederick H. Getman, *The Life of Ira Remsen* (Easton, Pennsylvania, 1940), 116; *National Cyclopaedia*, 13:26. The *National Cyclopaedia* survey showed that better than one-half of all the chemists who found work in industry in the years 1850-70 were men without any specialized training in the science. Some had received a classical school education and some had had no education beyond the high school level—if that.

61. The *National Cyclopaedia* survey showed that in this period, 12 chemists founded their own businesses and 15 took jobs in established firms.

mid-1850's Cyrus Warren, Lawrence Scientific School graduate and one-time student at European universities, established the Warren Chemical and Manufacturing Company. In 1866 William Warner, trained at the Philadelphia College of Pharmacy, founded a drug concern which pioneered in the manufacture of the sugar-coated pill. In the 1870's David Hiscox likewise set up a drug manufacturing firm. Hiscox, however, prepared himself for this business venture by an apprenticeship with a druggist.[62]

As the training of these four chemists illustrated, the level of technological development in the third quarter of the nineteenth century gave a man with no formal training in chemistry as easy access to manufacturing as it did the chemist with specialized preparation. E. R. Squibb was a case in point. In the mid-1840's Squibb, a doctor of medicine, began a period of service as a naval surgeon. During his tour of duty he obtained authority to set up a small laboratory to manufacture the pharmaceuticals and chemicals he needed in his work. Squibb was soon manufacturing ether, chloroform, salts, and acids in his Navy laboratory. In 1857 the Navy refused him further funds, whereupon he left the service. A year later, urged on by the promise of an Army contract, Squibb established a firm to manufacture chemicals and drugs. After weathering an initial period of difficulty, the firm of Edward R. Squibb, M.D., rapidly became one of the nation's leading pharmaceutical houses.[63]

The position of the chemist in industry in the years from 1870 to the end of the century was little changed from what it had been in the preceding 25 years. Although there were nearly 9000 chemists in the United States at the end of the nineteenth century, all of the chemical industries combined employed only 276 of them full time.[64] In the last quarter of the century American industry underwent a process of concentration of control and expansion of operations, yet industrialists remained reluctant to hire trained

62. *National Cyclopaedia*, 10:313; 2:167; 1:472. 63. *DAB*, 17:487-88.
64. Bureau of the Census, *Occupations at the Twelfth Census*, xxxiv-xxxv; Bureau of the Census, *Manufactures* (Washington, 1902), Part 4:528. The industries surveyed under the heading "Chemical Industries" were the chemical manufacturing firms (those making soda, potash, explosives, general chemicals, dyestuffs, paints, etc.), not the chemical process industries (petroleum, steel, salt, sugar, etc.); however, one can safely make the assumption —at least for the year 1900—that the former group of industries would be most amenable to the employment of chemists, and would thus hire the bulk of them. The *National Cyclopaedia* survey corroborates this.

chemists. The managers of American industries simply felt that chemistry had nothing to offer them. Rule of thumb methods and a native mechanical genius continued to earn substantial profits, and the great abundance of resources made it generally unnecessary to practice refinements in production methods or to minimize waste.[65]

Andrew Carnegie, describing the state of scientific control in the iron and steel industry in the 1870's, said that "chemistry was almost an unknown agent in connection with the manufacture of pig iron." The blast furnace manager "was usually a rude bully," who was "supposed to diagnose the condition of the furnace by instinct, to possess some almost supernatural power of divination. . . . He was a veritable quack doctor who applied whatever remedies occurred to him for the troubles of his patient."[66] Long after Carnegie turned to chemical control for his mills, about 1872, the proprietors of other furnaces were still claiming that they "could not afford to employ a chemist."[67]

In the ceramic industry (bricks, cement, glass, and pottery) science made little impression through the whole of the nineteenth century. The average potter was not willing to concede that chemistry could do anything for him. What were actually chemical processes, the mixing of body and glaze and the firing in the kiln, did not seem so to the potter because he had done them "by rote so long as to lose their real significance."[68] In the pulp and paper industry the story was the same. In 1900 a chemist described the industry as one that had made no attempt to utilize by-products or to produce the most profitable products. Similar resistance to science prevailed in sugar refining. In the 1880's one chemist in the southern sugar industry found that chemical control was "practically unheard of, and the losses incident to the manufacture were almost absolutely unknown."[69]

65. For the appraisal by contemporary American chemists of the reasons for industrial disdain for chemical control, see A. D. Little, "Industrial Research in America," *Journal of Industrial and Engineering Chemistry*, 5 (1913), 793; W. R. Whitney, "Chemical Research and Industrial Progress," American Electro-chemical Society, *Transactions*, 19 (1911), 23-26.

66. Carnegie, *Autobiography* (Boston, 1920), 181.

67. *Ibid.*, 182-3.

68. Edward Orton, "Progress of the Ceramic Industry," *Bulletin of the University of Wisconsin*, 2 (1903), 283.

69. Swensen, "The Chemical Engineer," *Bulletin of the University of Wisconsin*, 2 (1900), 198, 200.

In the last quarter of the nineteenth century the position of the trained industrial chemist was not enviable. Firms which imposed some measure of scientific control over their processes as likely as not bypassed the professional and hired a nonskilled worker for the operation. If the chemist found a position he could seldom feel secure in his job, owing to industry's feeling that it could really do as well without the frills of science. The professional who managed to keep his post usually bought job security at the cost of tedium.[70]

One chemist who had the best training that the German universities could offer, and who had then worked three years in German chemical industry, experienced all manner of difficulty trying to earn a living in American industry. When he returned to the United States he had great difficulty finding a job. Then, in 1895, after he had obtained a place and worked in it for five years, he lost his position to the owner's son. Finding another place proved impossible. "I have tried to obtain a new one," he said, "for the last eight months, but in vain. I am conversant with the processes used in making all the leading chemicals . . . but can find no one who wants my services."[71]

Chemist Otto Eisenschiml managed to hold his position, and his work conditions were like those of most trained chemists in industry. Eisenschiml received his education at the technical institute in Vienna. In 1900 he got his first job in the laboratory of a Pittsburgh blast furnace. The laboratory had a staff of twelve men and not one, except Eisenschiml, had any formal training in chemistry. The laboratory chief, a former water boy who had worked up to his present position, conveyed the attitude of most of industry toward trained scientists when he warned Eisenschiml that he didn't "want no university nonsense around here."[72] Eisenschiml's work consisted of two tasks, the testing of iron for phosphorus and the analysis of slag for iron, and he performed them day in and day out.[73] He had occasion to meet with chemists in other Pittsburgh industries and "they were no better off than their colleagues in the iron and steel works. Some were college graduates, others were not; it did not seem to make much difference." Not

70. A. D. Little, "Industrial Research in America," *Journal of Industrial and Engineering Chemistry*, 5 (1913), 798; C. L. Reese, "Industrial Benefits of Research," *Circular of the National Research Council* (Washington, 1921), 3.
71. J.O.L., "The Career of a Chemist," *Scientific American*, 72 (1895), 130.
72. Eisenschiml, *Without Fame*, 63; also see 63-67.
73. *Ibid.*, 78-79, 68.

only were work conditions generally poor but salaries were equally bad. According to Eisenschiml pawn-brokers, clerks, "even streetcar conductors and nightwatchmen were paid better than chemists."[74]

In the last quarter of the nineteenth century, however, American industry gradually began to change its attitude toward the need of chemical services. The shift was almost imperceptible before the late 1880's.[75] Although no single year marked the beginning of industry's acceptance of chemistry, the economic developments of the 1870's and 1880's prepared the ground for it. The depression beginning in 1873 greatly weakened or brought about the collapse of many small manufacturing establishments and permitted the stronger firms to absorb their less stable competitors. The consolidation of American industry into larger and larger units of production provided the capital to develop new and intricate processes and to employ the skilled technicians to operate them.

Many factors spurred industry to give a willing ear to the claims of science. The pre-eminence of the German chemical industry heightened an awareness in America of what might be done with a greater use of chemists and the methods of chemical science. The pressures of national and foreign competition that came with the rise of national industry forced industrialists to pay heed to production costs, process improvement, and utilization of waste products. And the adoption of technological improvements in one industry usually forced other industries to undertake similar improvements.[76] Setting the pace in seeking the services of the chemist were the basic chemical industries (the producers of such products as pure chemicals, paints, dyes, and drugs), the chemical process industries (petroleum refining and metal manufacturing, with the exception of iron and steel), and certain others not identifiable as chemical or chemical process industries (notably the meat-packing and electrical industries).

74. *Ibid.,* 106.

75. A graphical plot of employment in industry (for non-proprietors), taking into account the year of employment, for the chemists of the *National Cyclopaedia* survey showed a heavier concentration of industrial positions beginning about 1885.

76. See Bureau of the Census, *Manufactures* (1902), 527-8; Swensen, 198-202; Little, 793; Eisenschiml, 75-76, 130-37; V. Grignard, "The Collaboration of Science and Industry," *Journal of Industrial and Engineering Chemistry,* 10 (1918), 137; John D. Rockefeller, *Random Reminiscences of Men and Events* (New York, 1933), 81-82.

The growing willingness of American industry to turn to science not only meant more jobs for chemists, but it carried with it a recognition of the academically trained specialist over the chemist who had only on-the-job experience.[77] The advice of the *Scientific American* to young men interested in industrial careers reflected the growing opportunity for trained specialists. In 1895 that magazine declared that of all branches of technology, the field of technical chemistry "offered the greatest opportunity for a successful career." Success, however, was contingent upon having the proper training; the *Scientific American* told the young reader that his first step should be to secure an education at some technical school like the Armour Institute or the Massachusetts Institute of Technology.[78]

Not only were there quantitative changes in the relationship of the trained chemist to American industry but there were qualitative changes as well. The first industrial chemists did routine work, keeping watch on existing processes and maintaining control over products by the use of standard analytical methods. Near the end of the nineteenth century chemists in some industries began to add to their duties those of new product development, which involved a degree of applied research. Finally, in the early twentieth century, a few industries began to allow their chemists to engage in basic research in connection with product development. Not all industries which accepted the trained chemist to do routine work advanced to the second stage by the 1890's or to the third stage by the early 1900's, but the tendency toward these changes was broadly evident in industry.

The careers of Charles B. Dudley, Charles McDowell, and Willis R. Whitney illustrated these changes in the industrial concept of the chemist's function. Dudley was probably the first man to serve in a department of railroad chemistry. In 1875 the Pennsylvania Railroad hired him to set up purchasing standards for all the products that the railroad bought and to test incoming goods to insure that they met company specifications. When Dud-

77. The *National Cyclopaedia* survey showed that of 18 chemists who made industrial work their life's career (employment for 25 years or more), 17 of them began work after 1870. Of the 31 chemists who held industrial jobs for any length of time at all (after 1870), 28 had specialized academic training in chemistry. For the period before 1870 by contrast, only 7 of 15 chemists had this kind of training.
78. "On the Choice of a Career," *Scientific American*, 72 (1895), 34.

ley entered upon this work there was little understanding in any industry of the relationship between the chemical composition of an article and the quality of its performance. Dudley's work, the testing of goods and the return of articles which failed to meet specifications, aggravated the railroad's suppliers, but it forced them in the end "to protect their interests and defend their materials by means of testing engineers [namely, chemists] in their own employ."[79]

In 1887 Charles McDowell joined the firm of Armour and Company. At that time the leading packing firms were getting into the by-products business. Competition among the large packers was behind this development. As Louis Swift, son of the Swift and Company founder, said, the "keen competition . . . among the large concerns [in meat packing] forced down prices and forced down margins. Unless one kept abreast of the others in by-product utilization, then that laggard inevitably went under."[80] McDowell's assignment at Armour was to develop a line of products from materials formerly regarded as waste. Under the touch of chemistry, blood, bone fragments, and dried meat offal became profitable fertilizer constituents. Hides and bones yielded up glue, gelatin, and grease.[81]

Willis R. Whitney was the first director of the General Electric research laboratory. In this capacity he served a firm which was the recognized leader in the industrial research movement. The companies which made the earliest ventures into research were the chemical, chemical process, and electrical industries—DuPont, Bell Telephone, Westinghouse, Eastman Kodak, and Standard Oil (Indiana). These were the "new" industries in the sense that they arose as a result of nineteenth-century scientific discoveries, rather than by the slow development of time-honored craft techniques. Getting their start from science and dependent upon it, these industries did not show the older industries' reluctance to adopt scientific controls and methods.[82]

79. Dudley, in a speech before the American Society for Testing Materials (ASTM), quoted in ASTM, *Charles B. Dudley* (Philadelphia, 1911), 165; see also 20-23, 50-52, 165.

80. *Yankee of the Yards* (Chicago, 1927), 12; *National Cyclopaedia*, A:121.

81. William Haynes, *American Chemical Industry* (6 volumes, New York City), 6:415; United States Census, *Report on Manufacturing Industries in the United States* (Washington, 1895), 561.

82. Kendall Birr, *Pioneering in Industrial Research* (Washington, 1957), 8, 20.

In 1900, in an effort to rebuild its position of technical leadership in the industry, General Electric founded a laboratory "devoted exclusively to original research."[83] The company selected W. R. Whitney, then professor of chemistry at the Massachusetts Institute of Technology, as director and gave him a free hand to choose his own staff.

Although the work of the laboratory always had a practical end ultimately in view, the investigating team approached problems at the level of theory. In that way Whitney and his staff not only got the results wanted by General Electric but also added significantly to the knowledge of chemistry in the process. "We see a field," said Whitney, "where it seems as though experimental work ought to put us ahead. . . . We start back at the academic end as far as possible, and count on knowing what to do with what we find when we find it. Suppose that we surmise that . . . combustible insulation material could be improved upon. We try to get some work started on an artificial mica. Maybe we try to synthesize it and soon come to a purely theoretical question. . . . This may lead a long way and call in a lot of pure chemistry. . . . Usually we keep at it, so that if you haven't seen it on the market we're probably at it yet."[84]

By the second decade of this century industrial acceptance of the scientist overcame traditional disdain as the dominant attitude of American industry. In 1910 Ira Remsen, president of the Johns Hopkins University, noted the passing of an old attitude and the establishment of a new. The Johns Hopkins, he said, could not produce chemists fast enough to satisfy the calls of American industries. In fact industrial positions were so attractive that it was becoming difficult for Hopkins to supply the demand for teachers. The moral was plain, Remsen declared: the "chemical industries of the United States have learned the lesson . . . that their hope of success lies in the adoption of the most scientific methods possible."[85]

* * * * *

The modern American chemistry profession is firmly rooted to the institutional developments of the last half of the nineteenth century. The value system of present-day chemistry had its

83. GE technical director E. W. Rice, quoted in *Birr*, 31.
84. Quoted in Little, 796.
85. Quoted in Getman, 122-23.

beginnings in that earlier period. Research-mindedness was not a product of the present century: as early as the 1860's men like Wolcott Gibbs saw research as the proper concern of the student and the professional man. Although the non-Ph.D. chemist could easily find work in the nineteenth century, the trend toward hiring the highly trained specialist for government service and academic positions began long before 1900. When Ira Remsen gathered his faculty at the Johns Hopkins University, he considered only those chemists who could submit evidence (namely, a Ph.D. degree) of research ability. An eagerness to publish, a corollary of research, also marked the profession in its early period. Remsen's conviction that no suitable outlet existed for American investigation led him to found the *American Chemical Journal*. Its success showed that American workers were publication-conscious. Frank Clarke won support for a revitalized national society largely on the ground that such an organization could maintain a strong chemical journal. By 1900 the trend toward increasing specialization within the profession, which has reached such heights today, was already apparent. In the 1890's the professor of physical chemistry replaced the professor of chemistry, just as the latter, several decades earlier, had replaced the natural philosopher. In 1895 the appearance of an abstract of American chemical research gave evidence that even nineteenth-century professionals had trouble keeping abreast of the literature.

If American chemists in the twentieth century made outstanding contributions to their science and to the larger American society, investments of time and energy by nineteenth-century workers made these achievements possible. In a day of government generosity and strong private support of science, in a time of vigorous professional organization and security of position, American chemists tend to forget that workers did not always operate amid such plenty. Modern-day professionals readily acknowledge their debt to those earlier workers who laid the theoretical foundations of chemistry. The pioneer chemists who built the institutional foundations of the American profession deserve equal credit. Had the nineteenth-century workers not labored to erect departments of chemistry, journals, and societies, American chemistry would not occupy the position of influence that it does today.

Lacking adequate support, laboring against the traditional attitudes that thwarted their efforts, and often toiling without the satisfaction of seeing the fruits of their work, the nineteenth-century pioneers created the professional machinery that was essential if American workers were ever to make major contributions to chemical theory. From 1931 to 1961 twelve American chemists won the Nobel Prize, as compared to a combined total of fifteen for the Germans and English.[86] The success of American investigators in winning so many of these distinguished awards was a tribute to the efforts of earlier generations of professional workers who had built a solid foundation for the American chemistry profession.

86. Harry Hansen, ed., *The World Almanac and Book of Facts* (New York, 1962), 562-63.

NOTE ON THE SOURCES

The footnotes provide a listing of all sources used. Scientific periodicals and the proceedings of scientific societies were the most reliable and valuable guides. *The American Journal of Science and Arts, The American Chemist, The American Chemical Journal,* and *The Journal of the American Chemical Society* were especially useful for the story of the development of chemical publications. For reports of the research, organization building, and educational activities of American chemists, *The American Journal of Science and Arts* was indispensable because it was the only one spanning the entire period from 1850 to 1900. The editorial sections of *The American Chemist* reported in greater detail the day-to-day work of profession building. Volume 5 (1875), 43-115, 119-209, 327-28, featured the Centennial Celebration of chemists. The general usefulness of the periodical was limited, however, because it had such a brief existence.

Frank W. Clarke's article, "The Chemical Work of the United States Geological Survey," in *Science,* 30 (August, 1909), 161-71, provided a first-hand account of chemists' activity in this branch of government service. Clarke's essay showed that by the 1880's the chemist in government service had won recognition as a scientific specialist. A. D. Little's article, "Industrial Research in America," in the *Journal of Industrial and Engineering Chemistry,* 5 (1913), 783-801, offered a historical account of industrial acceptance of the chemist. A series of exchanges between an unnamed editor and an anonymous correspondent, "On the Choice of a Career," in *Scientific American,* 72 (1895), 34, 130, 211, provided a helpful commentary on the position of the chemist in industry at the turn of the century. The discussion very neatly illustrated the dichotomy in the attitude of industry toward chemists at that time. The *Scientific American* as a whole was of little use in studying the developing chemistry profession, for it was largely a journal of technological innovation. Ezra Carr's address, "The Claims of the Natural Sciences to Enlarged Considerations in our System of Education," in the *Publications of the Chemistry Department of the University of Wisconsin,* 1 (1855-99), 59-77, was a valuable commentary on the state of higher education in the middle of the nineteenth century and on the movement for practical education.

The first volume of the *Proceedings of the American Chemical Society* (1877) told the full story of the beginnings of that organization. Later efforts to build a stronger national society were chronicled in the *Proceedings of the American Association for the Advancement of Science*, volumes 37-39 (1889-91). The addresses of the chairmen of the American Association's chemical section, in that body's *Proceedings*, described the work of leading chemists who were trying to set standards and attack the problems of their profession. Charles Loring Jackson and Charles W. Eliot's obituary of Josiah Parsons Cooke in the *Proceedings of the American Academy of Arts and Sciences*, 30 (1895), 513-47, offered the most complete published account of the early development of education in chemistry at Harvard College.

The *Journal of Chemical Education*, a more recent publication, contained two collections of source material not available elsewhere. Edgar Fahs Smith's biography of Charles Meyer Wetherill in 6 (1929), 1076, 1215, 1461, 1668, 1916, 2160, contained many of the letters of a man whose varied career in private consulting work, government service, and teaching reflected the occupational prospects of the chemist of the 1850's and 1860's. C. A. Browne's article, "The European Laboratory Experiences of an Early American Agricultural Chemist—Dr. Evan Pugh," in 7 (March, 1930), 499-517, contained many of Pugh's letters, which gave an intimate view of American students' experiences in Germany.

Much of the story of the developing profession could be found in collections of unpublished correspondence. The Stephen Moulton Babcock Papers at the Wisconsin State Historical Library, Madison, Wisconsin, showed the research opportunity afforded the chemist by the agricultural experiment stations. Babcock's correspondence with his family and with other chemists during the 1870's and 1880's offered an accurate picture of American students' experiences in Germany, and of the position of the chemist in American higher education. The letters of Benjamin Silliman, Jr., and John Pitkin Norton to their former student, William H. Brewer, and to the Yale Corporation, are located in the Memorabilia Collection of the Yale University Library, New Haven, Connecticut. The correspondence with Brewer dealt with the general state of chemistry in America in the 1850's and contained the Yale chemists' reflections on European study and on the endowment of scientific education. The letters to the Yale Corporation dealt with the establishment of the scientific department, and related the trials, hopes, and successes of the two men most responsible for its development. A record of the early official correspondence from the Yale chemistry laboratory was found in the Letter Press Book of the Yale Analytical Laboratory, at the Yale University Library. A microfilm copy of these letters is on deposit at the Wisconsin Historical Society Library. The letters from Norton and Silliman for the most part discussed such matters as equipment and materials purchases, and were of little use to the story of professional development. There were, however, some letters from Norton to prospective students and others which described the course program and its aim, revealing Norton's hopes for education in chemistry at the Yale scientific school.

Official reports of government agencies and universities constituted another important body of source material. The *Circulars of Information* of the United States Office of Education contained many of the statistics on education in chemistry. Frank W. Clarke's *Report on the Teaching of Chemistry and Physics in the United States* in *Circular* number 6 (1881) provided a complete survey of educational facilities and a description of the chemistry departments of every higher educational institution in the nation. In 1888 the Office of Education began the publication in its *Circulars* of the history of higher education in the several states. While little attention was focused specifically on chemistry, the histories provided good accounts of scientific education at the major universities. C. W. Hayes' compilation, *The State Geological Surveys of the United States,* in the United States Geological Survey *Bulletin* number 465 (1911), 177 pp., offered a capsule history of all the state surveys and was of use in assessing the role of the chemist in that movement. The *Bulletins of the Division of Chemistry,* published by the United States Department of Agriculture, contained the proceedings of the Association of Official Agricultural Chemists. Although most of this material related to the chemists' efforts to erect analytical standards, *Bulletin* number 24 (1890), 66-68, featured an address by Frank W. Clarke on a proposed national chemical society. Clarke's address was an important part of the story of chemical society building.

University catalogues are lifeless affairs, but they provided a helpful guide to the changes that took place in American higher education during the third quarter of the nineteenth century. Yale and Harvard University *Catalogues* for the period 1845-65 revealed the character and aim of instruction in the Sheffield and Lawrence Scientific schools and pointed up the contrast between scientific instruction in academic colleges and that in scientific schools. The Harvard *Catalogues* for 1850-60 detailed the work of Josiah Cooke in enlarging the chemistry curriculum at Harvard College, but they were totally silent on the chemistry laboratory that Cooke organized and which was such an important part of his total contribution. The *Official Circulars* of the Johns Hopkins University for 1876 and 1877 provided a concise statement of the educational philosophy of that institution. Ira Remsen's plans for chemistry at the Johns Hopkins appeared in the sections of the *Circulars* pertaining to his own department.

Very few autobiographies of American chemists exist. Harvey Wiley's *Autobiography* (Indianapolis, 1930), 339 pp., and Otto Eisenschiml's *Without Fame: The Romance of a Profession* (Chicago, 1942), 368 pp., were two colorful exceptions. Together, these books afforded an intimate look at the American chemist in his many roles: student, teacher, profession builder, government worker, and industrial employee. Elizabeth Osborne's *From the Letter Files of Samuel W. Johnson* (New Haven, 1918), an edition of her father's correspondence, provided a very human picture of the expectations and disappointments of the German-trained scholars who attempted to establish the research tradition in American universities in the middle of the nineteenth century.

The National Academy of Sciences' *Memoirs* and *Biographical Memoirs* contained reasonably adequate biographical sketches of influential nineteenth-century chemists. Unfortunately, there was little about the individual's contribution to the institutional development of his profession. Most of the memoirs concentrated on contributions of a technical nature and otherwise tended to be too concerned with eulogizing the departed to be of much historical worth. Those of Wolcott Gibbs, 7 (1913), 1-22; W. F. Hillebrand, 12 (1929), 43-70; Ira Remsen, 14 (1932), 210-30; and Charles F. Chandler, 14 (1932), 127-84, were exceptions.

The *National Cyclopaedia of American Biography* was an extremely useful source. The biographies of about 250 chemists, active in the nineteenth century, appeared here. While not providing

73

biographical information as complete as the National Academy's *Memoirs*, the *Cyclopaedia* contained more vital statistics on more chemists than were available in any other source. Sifting the information offered here produced a clear picture of the changing pattern of education and employment of American chemists during the nineteenth century. A survey of all the chemists featured in the *Cyclopaedia* yielded a close approximation of the activity of the whole body of American chemists. The chronology of professional development, resulting from such a survey, aided in setting this development in its proper social perspective.

Secondary works provided a grasp of the broader social framework in which nineteenth-century American chemists functioned. Richard J. Storr's *The Beginnings of Graduate Education in America* (Chicago, 1953), 195 pp., was an important study of the pre-Civil-War origins of the university movement, focusing attention on the developing pressures for more practical education. Richard Hofstadter and C. Dewitt Hardy's *The Development and Scope of Higher Education in the United States* (New York, 1952), 254 pp., and Frederick Rudolph's *The American College and University* (New York, 1962), 516 pp., took up the scientific-school movement and continued the story of educational reform through and beyond the founding of the Johns Hopkins University. The movement for agricultural education and its implications for education in the basic sciences was well covered in Earle D. Ross, *Democracy's College: The Land-Grant Movement in the Formative Years* (Ames, Iowa, 1942), 267 pp. A. Hunter Dupree, in *Science in the Federal Government* (Cambridge, 1957) 460 pp., traced the development of government sponsorship of science and described the evolution of the scientific bureaus which provided a home for American chemists.

Samuel Eliot Morison gave a clear but abbreviated account of the development of scientific education in the Lawrence Scientific School and in Harvard College, in his *Three Centuries of Harvard, 1636-1936* (Cambridge, 1937), 512 pp. The development of chemistry at the Sheffield Scientific School received detailed coverage by physiological chemist, Russell H. Chittenden, in his *History of the Sheffield Scientific School* (2 volumes, New Haven, 1928), 610 pp. Chittenden's work was overly statistical but it provided the background needed for a proper reading of the correspondence of the pioneer Yale chemists.

74

Friedrick Paulsen's *German Universities: Their Character and Historical Development* (New York, 1895), 254 pp., was a cold and antiseptic account of the German university, its philosophy, methods, and structure. But for a clear understanding of the German educational environment in which American students trained, the book had no peer. Charles Thwing's *The American and the German University* (New York, 1928), 238 pp., was a more humanized treatment of the same subject. It was helpful for the picture it gave of American students' reaction to their German experiences.

Nearly all secondary works dealing with chemists or the chemistry profession were internal histories. There were, however, a few exceptions. John F. Fulton and Elizabeth H. Thompson's *Benjamin Silliman, 1779-1864, Pathfinder in American Science* (New York, 1947), 294 pp., was a good biography and treated Silliman's role in establishing the Yale School of Applied Chemistry and his work in scientific journalism. The limitation of the book for purposes of the present study was that the central figure, although a prominent chemist, passed from the scene in the early stages of professional development. Charles A. Browne and Mary Elvira Week's *History of the American Chemical Society* (Washington, 1952), 526 pp., was very useful for its detailed footnoting and statistical information, but it romanticized the work of society building. Frederick H. Getman's *Life of Ira Remsen* (Easton, Pennsylvania, 1940), 172 pp., contained some of Remsen's letters and addresses, but its use was limited by a complete absence of footnotes and bibliography. The Massachusetts Agricultural College's commemorative biography, *Charles Anthony Goessmann* (Cambridge, 1917), 187 pp., was a brief but well-written account of a man who was at various times a German university instructor, industrial chemist, American College teacher, and experiment station director.

75

UNIVERSITY OF FLORIDA MONOGRAPHS

Social Sciences

No. 1 (Winter 1959): *The Whigs of Florida, 1845-1854.* By Herbert J. Doherty, Jr.

No. 2 (Spring 1959): *Austrian Catholics and the Social Question, 1918-1933.* By Alfred Diamant

No. 3 (Summer 1959): *The Siege of St. Augustine in 1702.* By Charles W. Arnade

No. 4 (Fall 1959): *New Light on Early and Medieval Japanese Historiography.* By John A. Harrison

No. 5 (Winter 1960): *The Swiss Press and Foreign Affairs in World War II.* By Frederick H. Hartmann

No. 6 (Spring 1960): *The American Militia: Decade of Decison, 1789-1800.* By John K. Mahon

No. 7 (Summer 1960): *The Foundation of Jacques Maritain's Political Philosophy.* By Hwa Yol Jung

No. 8 (Fall 1960): *Latin American Population Studies.* By T. Lynn Smith

No. 9 (Winter 1961): *Jacksonian Democracy on the Florida Frontier.* By Arthur W. Thompson

No. 10 (Spring 1961): *Holman Versus Hughes: Extension of Australian Commonwealth Powers.* By Conrad Joyner

No. 11 (Summer 1961): *Welfare Economics and Subsidy Programs.* By Milton Z. Kafoglis

No. 12 (Fall 1961): *Tribune of the Slavophiles: Konstantin Aksakov.* By Edward Chmielewski

No. 13 (Winter 1962): *City Managers in Politics: An Analysis of Manager Tenure and Termination.* By Gladys M. Kammerer, Charles D. Farris, John M. DeGrove, and Alfred B. Clubok

No. 14 (Spring 1962): *Recent Southern Economic Development as Revealed by the Changing Structure of Employment.* By Edgard S. Dunn, Jr.

No. 15 (Summer 1962): *Sea Power and Chilean Independence.* By Donald E. Worcester

No. 16 (Fall 1962): *The Sherman Antitrust Act and Foreign Trade.* By Andre Simmons

No. 17 ((Winter 1963): *The Origins of Hamilton's Fiscal Policies.* By Donald F. Swanson

No. 18 (Spring 1963): *Criminal Asylum in Anglo-Saxon Law.* By Charles H. Riggs, Jr.

No. 19 (Summer 1963): *Colonia Barón Hirsch, A Jewish Agricultural Colony in Argentina.* By Morton D. Winsberg

No. 20 (Fall 1963): *Time Deposits in Present-Day Commercial Banking.* By Lawrence L. Crum

No. 21 (Winter 1964): *The Eastern Greenland Case in Historical Perspective.* By Oscar Svarlien

No. 22 (Spring 1964): *Jacksonian Democracy and the Historians.* By Alfred A. Cave

No. 23 (Summer 1964): *The Rise of the American Chemistry Profession, 1850-1900.* By Edward H. Beardsley